THE LAND OF KERFUFFLE

A Play for Christmas

Book and Lyrics by
BILL GAVIN

Music by
Ronald Corp and Vincent Zaniewski

SAMUEL   FRENCH

LONDON
NEW YORK   TORONTO   SYDNEY   HOLLYWOOD

THE LAND OF KERFUFFLE

First produced at the Aberdeen Arts Centre by the Aberdeen Mobile Theatre

Characters

Penny

Snowman

Fairy

Crocodile*

Mrs Penguin

Cockatoo

Fish

Doctor-in-Law

Mandarin

First Seal*

Second Seal*

Third Seal*

Minstrel

Gardener

The Great Panjandrum

Carol Singers

* Two of these characters, depending on their build in comparison with that of the Cockatoo and the Gardener, should be cast also as **Reserve Cockatoo** and **Reserve Gardener** (non-speaking parts), but this should not be acknowledged in the programme

The action of the play takes place between Christmas Eve and Christmas Dawn

ACT I

Scene 1   A Garden by Moonlight

Scene 2   Penny's Room

Time—the present

PRODUCTION NOTES

ACT I, Scene 1

The bank can be a cut-out, stretching from off stage, where it is about 4 ft high, to somewhere about the centre of the stage, where it reaches ground level. Two Christmas trees are required for the setting, one small and one large—say 3–4 ft, and about 6 ft or higher. The smaller of the two is set in the window, on top of the tea-trolley which is used in Act III. One side only of this tree should be decorated—the side facing the audience when the Curtain rises. If facilities permit, the fairy on top can be made revolvable by a simple reel-and-thread system operated from off stage, but this is not essential. The other side of this tree is quite bare.

The larger tree should be set just behind the cut-out bank, which will mask the fact that it is set on an industrial "skip". If it is not possible to borrow a skip from some local factory, warehouse or large store, one can quite simply be made from a board, roughly 18–24 in square, on to which four casters have been fitted, or even a pair of skateboards with their wheels suitably adjusted to make the "skip" revolvable. When the Curtain rises the front of the tree (facing the audience) should be snow-covered, possibly using cottonwool. The upstage side should be decorated like the tree in the window, with its "fairy" (a cardboard cut-out, possibly enhanced by a dusting of sparkle) stuck in the top-most branches and lightly held there by a fixative of Blu-tack variety. To facilitate this fairy's disappearance, it should be threaded to off stage by light, nylon fishing-line, which will merely require pulling during the appropriate lighting-dip.

An enhancement to both trees would be their decoration with fairy-lights. If this is not possible a liberal distribution of lustrous baubles would serve, as these will shine and glow in the existing light, and thus save wiring up.

Immediately behind the bank there should be one of the stools from Act II, on which the Snowman can sit, and the Fairy stand.

ACT I, Scene 2

In the interests of the magic in this scene each random item has a length of thin, nylon fishing-line attached to it, the other end of which, labelled with the name of the item to which it pertains, is off stage, mostly, for the clothing, behind the wardrobe. Others, attached to comics, for instance, could lead off via under-the-bed. If practical the "magic" can be extended to include more solid objects—a chair pulling itself under a desk, a cushion pulling itself from the floor on to a chair, a book on the table closing itself. The smoothness of the operation can almost be guaranteed if each of the helpers off stage is made responsible for placing the article or articles for

which they are personally responsible, and if all are laid down in reverse
order to that in which they are to be spirited away.

If a Nodding Mandarin is not procurable, a nodding toy can be easily
adapted by the addition of a Chinese hat and robe, made out of suitable
paper/material. These should be of the same colour as the real Mandarin's
costume in Act II.

ACT II, Scene 1

As there will be several variations on the Fish's hat gag in this and sub-
sequent scenes, the hat should be prepared beforehand by inserting inside,
close to the crown, two plastic drinking straws, one running from front
to back and the other from side to side. There should also be a tiny hole
in the front brim, the purpose of which becomes clear later. For the
present gag, the hat should be threaded through from side to side (using
nylon fishing-line); the line is drawn taut at the Fish's head level and the
ends firmly fixed behind bush and hedge. This means that when the Fish
moves from his opening position, by easing his head down—as if concentrating on a catch from the river—he will walk away without his hat,
leaving it, apparently, in mid-air. For his exit wearing the hat later on, the
stage management snip the thread at either end, once his head has been
pushed into the hat.

If the Cockatoo is unable to whistle, tiny mouth whistles are easily
obtainable.

ACT II, Scene 3

When the scene opens the Fish is already seated on his high-backed chair,
and his hat has been pre-threaded—from front to rear this time—with
nylon line. At the rear the line is securely fixed to the back of his seat at
his standing headlevel, but—since he is seated—there is a little slack
hanging down behind him. The remainder of the line (from the front of
the hat) is laid loosely along the floor, close to the steps leading to the
rostrum so as to prevent it from being caught up in the action, and it
finishes up off stage. As the Fish rises at the end of the scene, the line is
gently pulled taut by the stage management. About half-way across the
stage, the Fish lowers his head to blow open the next page of his comic.
This movement frees him from the hat and he walks off, leaving it in
mid-air.

If numbers in the Company allow, the procession can be elaborated by
attendant pages, other animals, etc. All would be non-speaking, except
for crowd effects. If a really spectacular procession is envisaged, an
entrance might be made through the auditorium with instrumentalists,
clowns, tumblers, etc.

If the actor playing the Panjandrum has naturally long hair, the effect
of his "half-shorn" head can be accomplished by brushing half his hair
flat, then holding it in position with hair-grips. For a short-haired actor
it merely means the addition of crêpe hair, as necessary.

ACT III, Scene 1

The log should be placed far enough downstage to serve in Scene 2, and attached to nylon thread so that it can be pulled off on cue.

To facilitate some of the "magic" in this act, the players selected to play the Reserve Gardener and Reserve Cockatoo should be in duplicate costumes of Gardener and Cockatoo as the Curtain rises. Do note that on p. 42 after the Cockatoo and the Gardener exit they should be exchanging their costumes off stage as from then on they will be playing each other's parts.

The Fish's hat: slightly upstage of his line of travel, the nylon thread has been passed through the hat, front-to-back. Two assistants, one off stage at either end, hold the line horizontal on the line of travel, while together they gently raise and lower the line to give an undulating movement. The hat moves along the line by means of another thread, fixed to the front of the brim, the other end of that line being held by Fish in his "comic" hand. When he disappears from view he stops and turns and, on the Cockatoo's whistle, raises his end of the thread, thus tilting the hat. When the Cockatoo screeches, Fish quickly pulls the hat towards himself, off stage. When the gag is finished, the nylon line—with the hat—should be laid carefully behind the rostrum for future use.

ACT III, Scene 3

The moving trolley (with Chinese food) is worked by pulling on a nylon thread.

The Fish's entrance and exit: the gag is worked on the same principle as before, except that this time the hat is pulled off by an assistant. The appropriate length of nylon line can be fixed during Scene 2.

ACT III, Scene 5

In Act I this scene was set in front of the inner tabs: in Act III it is set behind them.

The Music
Music for the songs can be obtained from Samuel French Ltd.

ACT I

SCENE 1

A garden. Winter, moonlight

On one side is a snowy bank and on it a snow-covered tree which, if decorated, would do very well for a Christmas tree. On the opposite side is the lighted window of a house, with a practical window, cottage-type, which opens outwards. Inside the window there is a decorated Christmas tree, topped by a Christmas tree fairy

There is yet another part of the scenery—the Snowman. He is very practical, for he is one of the characters in the play, although—at first—he looks exactly like part of the scenery. He stands almost at the foot of the snowy bank and just before it, his costume as suggestive of a snowman as possible, with the appearance of a carrot for a nose, marbles for eyes and stones for buttons. He wears a battered top-hat, a long scarf and holey gloves. His stance, at the outset, is supplemented by pieces of white plastic foam, adding to the illusion by dropping off piecemeal when he moves

Before the CURTAIN *rises the Carol Singers can be heard. Their song swells as it does so. They carry a lantern, and are grouped near the window. (Alternatively they might enter through the auditorium and move on stage.) Penny, a young girl, is at the window listening. She opens it as the carol finishes.*

Leader of the Carol Singers (*stepping towards Penny, doffing his hat and holding it out*) Merry Christmas, Penny!
Penny (*dropping a coin in the hat*) And a Merry Christmas to you, too!
All Carollers Merry Christmas!

The Carol Singers turn to exit, gathering some snow as they walk. They snowball the Snowman. One of them is near enough to knock off the Snowman's hat

   The Carol Singers run off, laughing

Penny, during the above, starts to close the window, but has difficulty with the catch. The window is not quite closed when the Snowman speaks

Snowman Of all the cheek!
Penny (*opening the window again*) I beg your pardon?
Snowman Downright dicacity!
Penny Who's speaking?
Snowman I am.
Penny Who's I?
Snowman Me. (*He still does not move*)

Penny (*staring at the Snowman, realizing*) Oh! Er—just a moment.

Penny disappears from the window, and enters a moment later, slowing as she nears the Snowman and walking round him curiously

Did you say something?

Snowman (*turning his head very slowly to her*) Of course I said something! Wouldn't you, if someone had knocked your hat off? You ought to be grateful I didn't say a lot more! Oh go on—hurry up—put it on again! I shall catch my death of cold!

Penny titters

Snowman And just what, may I enquire, do you find amusing in that?

Penny A snowman—catching cold!

The Snowman sniffs indignantly and looks out front

Penny Oh, very well! (*She retrieves the hat and places it on his head*) There! (*Pause*) Well? Aren't you going to say "Thank you"?

Snowman (*on his dignity*) Thank you.

Penny You're welcome. (*She begins to depart, but stops and turns, surprised*) How come you can talk but you can't move?

Snowman (*turning his head slowly towards Penny*) To tell you the truth, I'm frozen stiff. You've no idea how it feels, standing out here. It's a perishing cold night.

Penny (*shivering slightly*) Y-yes. I suppose it is. I'm sorry. I didn't think . . .

Snowman No. That's the trouble with you humans. You think nothing at all of building a snowman, like me, out here in the garden, then—(*near to tears*)—leaving me—all alone—in the cold—and the dark!

Penny (*running to him*) Oh, you poor dear Snowman! Would you like to come inside for a little while?

Snowman (*suddenly cautious*) Have you got a—(*spelling*)—F-I-R-E in there?

Penny Naturally.

Snowman Then I'm not coming. I don't want heartburn. I'd just waste away.

Penny Oh rubbish! People don't waste away with heartburn!

Snowman I would.

Penny (*considering*) Ye-es, I suppose you might—you not being people. (*She has another idea*) A little hot soup, perhaps?

Snowman (*slowly turning his head away from her*) Let's pretend we never said that, shall we? And please try not to say words like H-O-T in my presence. They make me shiver with horripilation!

Penny (*at a loss*) Oh—sorry. What *can* I get you?

Snowman A little something from the fridge might not be unacceptable.

Penny Cold chicken?

Snowman Er—no. It would stick in my throat. And if there's anything I can't stand, it's robins in the morning, picking my teeth!

Penny A coke?

Snowman Do you want me covered with icicles? It would freeze on me!

Penny (*tentatively*) Ice cream?

Snowman Ah! Now! A little ice cream I think I could wrap myself round very well.

Penny starts to go

(*Calling after her*) Bring it to the window—a bucketful at a time!

Penny goes into the house

Slowly, with great effort, the Snowman begins to move, first his arms and then his legs, robot-like

For a few—gallons—of ice cream—(*he walks stiffly towards the window*) —and a dozen or so—lollies—I'd travel far! (*He reaches the window, and looks back the way he has come*) That's far! Ah, well. (*To the audience*) Nice little girl, isn't she?

Penny opens the window

Penny Here you are, Mr Snowman. (*She proffers a dish of ice cream, with a spoon*)

Snowman Fotheringay. That's the name. Call me Fotheringay. (*He takes the ice cream*) Ah! This is a life-saver!

Penny Fotheringay? What a funny name!

Snowman Is it? I thought it was a very nice name to choose. Quite the only possible kind of name for a gentleman like me, with a top-hat and gloves. (*Supping*) Mmmm—this is good!

Penny I should have thought, on a cold night like this, you'd have preferred something a little warmer.

Snowman (*spluttering ice cream*) There you go again! W-A-R-M . . . Don't say such words! The very thought of them gives me goose-pimples. And very silly that makes me look—a snowman covered with goose-pimples!

Penny giggles

It's not funny! (*To the audience*) You don't think it's funny, do you? A snowman covered with goose-pimples? Ah, well! (*To Penny*) Let's change the subject, shall we? What's Santa Claus bringing you?

Penny (*derogatorily*) Santa Claus!

Showman Don't you believe in Santa Claus?

Penny (*proudly*) I'm twelve! (*Or as young as the actress aims to get away with*)

Snowman What's that got to do with it? (*He shrugs*) Oh, well . . . (*He looks at the fairy on the tree in the window*) I suppose you don't believe in fairies, either?

Penny I used to. But not now. I'm much too grown up.

Snowman How very sad. But you'll still be expecting something for Christmas?

Penny Why not?

Snowman Why not, indeed? It seems a pity, though—about Santa Claus,

I mean—and the fairy. It takes away some of the magic, somehow. I suppose you'll be telling me next that you don't even hang up your stocking.

Penny Oh, well—one has to do *something* to amuse one's parents. It keeps them happy.

Snowman Well, of all the . . . Er—never mind. And just what, may I ask, do you hope to get for Christmas?

Penny I know what I'd like.

Snowman What?

Penny A kitten.

Snowman A kitten?

Penny Yes. A nice soft, furry, playful kitten.

Snowman Mmmm—a kitten for Christmas. Yes, I suppose you could do worse. Puppies now, I can't stand. Nasty little things! Always barking and scratching holes under snowmen's feet, making them topple! But a kitten . . .

Penny I've no-one to play with, you see, or talk to. So I thought a kitten . . .

Snowman Yes. Very nice. (*Handing back the dish*) Thank you very much for the ice cream. (*He turns away*)

Penny Where are you going?

Snowman Down the garden again. Where else? Snowmen don't *go* anywhere, do they? Not until . . . (*He stops, thinking*)

Penny (*with her hand on the window-latch, about to close it*) Good night, Mr Fotheringay.

Snowman (*bowing gravely and doffing his hat*) Good night, Miss Penny.

Penny closes the window and disappears

The music of the Snowman's song starts. The interior light in the cottage goes out, and a drifting cloud begins to blot out the moon, making the garden grow slightly darker

No, I'm not going anywhere, really. (*He moves forward*)

THE SNOWMAN'S SONG

(*Recitative*)
   For I'm a snowman—
   Just a snowman.
   Not for me the roving life of a get-up-and-go man.
(*Singing*)
   For you build me in the garden
   In the cold and frosty air,
   And at the bottom of the garden
   I only stand and stare,
(*Speaking, in a very matter-of-fact voice, and stamping his feet*)
   And my feet get cold!
(*Recitative*)
   I'm a snowman—

    Just a snowman—
    Made out of tiny drops of water, don't you know, man?
(*Singing*)
    Vaporized in tiny crystals
    Away up in the clouds,
    To fall on all the world below
    In soft, enfolding shrouds.
(*Speaking, matter-of-fact*)
    And my ears get so cold, they drop off!

He flicks off the pieces of plastic foam

(*Recitative*)
    I'm a snowman—
    Just a snowman—
    I'm not exactly cuddly, I'm too cold, man!
(*Singing*)
    For you could not, for instance,
    Take me in your bed at night.
    In the morning I'd be melted,
    And you'd be awfully wet!
(*Speaking, with a roguish chuckle*)
    And wouldn't you
    Just cop it from your mums!
(*Recitative*)
    I'm a snowman—
    Just a snowman—
    Here today and gone tomorrow—I'm like no man!
(*Singing*)
    For one day, when you waken,
    I'll be just a small, wet ring
    On the ground where very shortly
    You'll see the flowers of spring.
(*Speaking soft, wistfully*)
    And I'll be gone.

Yes—I'll be gone. (*He looks at the fairy on the window tree*) I wish I
had a fairy to wish to! (*He sits on the bank, chuckling*) But wasn't that
odd—about Penny, I mean. She believes, apparently, in snowmen that
walk and talk—but she doesn't believe in fairies! (*To the audience*) Do
you believe in fairies? Do you? (*He waits for the response*) Ah well,
that's how it is, I suppose. Some do and some don't. (*He rises*) But
at least we can do something about Penny. Yes, and I might be able to
make my wish at the same time! But you'll have to help me. (*He crosses
the stage*)

*The Lights are now very low—almost the only light is that coming from the
tree in the window*

    (*As he crosses*) Let me see, I really need two wishes. First, I must wish
    me that fairy—and then I must wish me my own wish—for me! But

you must all wish with me. D'you know how to do it? You take a deep breath—like this. (*He inhales deeply and noisily, mouth wide open, then closes his mouth and eyes for a moment*) And you wish—hard! O.K.? Try it. One—two—deep breath! (*He breathes in*) Oh, come on, you can do better than that! I want to *hear* you breathing in. Try it again. One, two . . . (*He takes a deep breath*) That's better! Now, this time, we'll do it for real. Ready? One—two—wish hard. Wish me the fairy!

The fairy on the tree slowly begins to revolve—or a slightly wavering torch is trained on the fairy to make the tinsel sparkle

(*Opening his eyes*) Anything happened yet? (*He looks round*) Yes— look! The fairy's coming to life! But you're not wishing hard enough. We want her out here. Come on—try again! And this time—wish *really* hard. Ready? One—two—(*quickly*)—deep breath! Wish hard—hard!

The Lights momentarily fade to a Black-out. The lights on the Christmas tree go out and the tree is reversed. The fairy is snatched off. The tree in the garden is reversed, and the lights on it go on

(*Opening his eyes*) Have we done it? Have we? (*He looks round*) We have! (*Going to the garden tree, addressing the audience*) Oh, thank you —thank you, everyone! (*He sees both trees, and does a double-take*) But you've wished too hard. You've got me the tree as well! Never mind. (*He jumps up and down by the garden tree, clapping his hands*) Goodie, goodie, goodie, goodie, goodie! Now I can make my wish . . . (*He looks up at the fairy on the garden tree*) I hope! You *are* a real fairy, aren't you? (*Sincerely, putting one foot on the bank*) I believe in fairies.

The fairy twinkles

(*To the audience*) She's very still, isn't she? D'you think she could be frozen up there? Frozen stiff, I mean? I'm awfully cold out here in the garden. (*To the fairy*) And anyway, I don't know if it's any good my talking to you away up there—I don't even know if you can hear me.
Fairy (*off*) Shall I come down?

The Snowman looks at the fairy in amazement, his head on one side. He then looks straight out front, double-takes on the fairy, then speaks to the audience

Snowman Did you hear that? Or was I dreaming? (*He looks again at the fairy, first from one side of the tree, then from the other, stroking his chin, considering. To the audience*) Oh, I'd—er—I'd better answer, hadn't I. (*To the fairy*) Yes, please—come down.

The Lights fade to a Black-out, except for a pin-spot, during which the fairy is jerked off the tree in the darkness. They immediately come up again. The pin-spot meanwhile flits about in the air, a tiny speck of light, dancing first to the window-ledge, where it hovers for a moment, then back to touch the Snowman lightly on the head. Then it flits to the side of the stage, where it opens into a fuller spot on the Fairy

The Fairy enters from the wings, on the opposite side from the garden tree

The Snowman crosses to her slowly, in awe. As he nears her he puts out his hand as if to touch her

Fairy No—please! You must never touch a fairy. (*She crosses in front of him, towards the garden tree*)

Snowman Oh, I—er—I wouldn't! I just wanted to wish a wish.

Fairy Well?

Snowman It's not a very big wish. You see, I'm only a snowman, and—er . . .

Fairy Yes?

Snowman Well, you see, snowmen don't last very long, and I—I wondered if—when I'm not a snowman any more—if I could . . .

Fairy Go on.

Snowman If you could turn me into a . . . (*He hangs his head, interlocking his fingers, his body swinging from side to side, like a shy child*)

Fairy Into a what? (*She comes nearer him*) Turn you into a what, Mr Fotheringay? (*Gently*) I can't help you if you don't tell me.

The Snowman advances to the Fairy, whispers in her ear, then steps back, anxiously waiting

What a lovely wish!

Snowman Is it? I'm not being silly, am I?

Fairy Of course you're not. Why, it's a beautiful thought! I think, deep down, you must be a very happy person.

Snowman Oh, I am—I think!

Fairy Aren't you sure?

Snowman Well, I—suppose I must be. You see—people, when they build me, they're happy, aren't they? And other people, when they look at me, they smile. So I just wanted to go on—making people happy.

Fairy I think that's wonderful—you being so happy—and standing about in the cold, too, like you do. How do you manage it?

Snowman Oh, that's easy. I just—sing songs to myself.

Fairy Sing me one.

Snowman Now?

Fairy Yes. Sing me a song and I'll grant your wish. Tell me—about your happiness. (*She sits on the bank*)

Snowman All right. I will.

THE HAP-HAP-HAPPY SONG

(*Singing*)
I have a hap-hap-happy song
In the winter, deep and long!
When the wind, it blows,
And the snow, it snows,
This is my hap-hap-happy song!

When the trees are stark and bare,
And the frost it nips the air,
When your pipes are froze

> And you've tingling toes,
> You can see me anywhere!

He executes a little dance during the next verse

> With my hat upon my head,
> And my carrot-nose so red,
> I have two glass eyes,
> And—surprise, surprise—
> For buttons I have stones instead!
> (*"Whisper"-singing*)
> And in the cold and silent night,
> When all the world is still and white,
> I'll be there on guard
> In your own backyard,
> While you are all a-sleeping tight!
> (*Speaking aloud*) You lucky people!

He executes another little dance

> (*Singing, full voice*)
> So, if you pass me in the snow,
> Don't forget to say "Hullo"—
> Like a Christmas card,
> It's not very hard
> To spread a little friendly glow!

Fairy (*rising*) That's marvellous, Mr Fotheringay—it really is!
Snowman (*mock bashfully*) Oh, there's nothing to it. I just—toss off a song whenever I feel like it.

Penny appears at the window and opens it

Penny Hey! What have you done with my tree?
Snowman Oh—er—Penny—look who's here. (*He indicates the Fairy*)
Penny (*momentarily open-mouthed*) I'm coming out!

Penny disappears from the window

Snowman (*to the Fairy*) You must excuse Penny. She—er—she doesn't believe in—er—you.
Fairy (*flouncing on to the bank*) Well—really!

Penny enters behind the Snowman and peeps round him

Penny Who's she?
Snowman The Christmas Tree Fairy.
Penny (*in a lower tone*) How'd she get down?
Snowman (*also in a low tone*) She flew down.
Penny (*again quietly*) I don't believe it! Make her wave her wand.
Snowman (*to the Fairy, in a low tone*) Wave your wand.
Fairy I beg your pardon?
Snowman (*in his normal voice*) Oh—er—sorry! Ahem—please wave your wand.

The Fairy shrugs and waves her wand

Penny Well?
Snowman Well what?
Penny Nothing happened!
Fairy Did you expect it to?

Another cloud begins to blot out the moon

Penny You're supposed to be a Fairy, aren't you?
Snowman (*leading Penny aside by her arm*) You're supposed to wish a wish.
Penny (*matter-of-factly*) I wish she'd put my tree back where it belongs!
Fairy Certainly. (*She waves her wand at the garden tree*)
Penny Huh! Some fairy! She got my tree out in the garden and now she can't put it back again.
Snowman (*to the Fairy*) Can't you?
Fairy (*non-plussed*) I—don't know. This has never happened to me before! (*She waves her wand at the tree again, without result*)
Snowman Oh, please don't tell me you can't magic things any more!
Fairy I can't understand it. There seems to be something working against me.
Snowman (*turning slowly to look at Penny, and engaging the audience with his look*) Y-e-s—and we all know what that is, don't we? (*To Penny*) This is your fault!
Penny Mine?
Snowman For not believing in fairies!
Fairy It could be that. If it is, there's nothing to be done.
Snowman Oh yes, there is! We can get some help. (*He appeals to the audience*) Let's all help the Christmas Tree Fairy! Remember how you did it before—one, two, deep breath and wish? Right—we'll do the same again. Only, this time, you'll have to wish *much* harder—(*indicating Penny*)—because we've got opposition! So I'll tell you what we'll do. We'll close our eyes this time while we're wishing, and we'll wish the tree back into the window. Ready? One—two—deep breath! Close your eyes. And *wish*. Wish hard—hard! Are you all wishing hard?

The Lights are now very low

The Fairy, meanwhile, waves her wand and moves behind the tree, as she does so, she drops out of sight, and exits

Simultaneously, in a Black-out, the garden tree lights go out and it is reversed—then the window tree is reversed and its lights go on

(*Opening his eyes and looking round*) We've done it! We've done it! (*He grasps Penny's hands and dances her round, chanting*) The tree is in the window! The tree is in the window! (*He halts suddenly, facing the window*) Oh dear! Where's the fairy gone? (*He looks at Penny*)
Penny (*glancing round, then back at the Snowman*) Don't look at me. I haven't got it—er—her!

B

The Snowman and Penny seek around, moving to the front of the stage. The front tabs close behind them

Snowman She must be somewhere! I'll tell you what—you go that-a-way— (*pointing to one side*)—and I'll go this. (*He indicates the opposite side*)

They descend into the audience, searching. (If this is impossible, they speak from either side of the stage)

(*Calling to Penny*) She doesn't seem to be this side. Is she over there? **Penny** (*calling*) No, she's not here.

They speak ad lib. *to the audience*

Snowman Have you seen her?
Penny Did she come this way?
Snowman Are you sure?
Penny Has no-one at all seen her?

}*etc.*

Snowman (*calling to the back of the house or the balcony*) She's not back up there, is she? (*Generally*) Look under your seats, everyone. She might be under a seat somewhere. Are you quite sure she isn't? Oh, you can't be looking properly! Search your pockets!

The Snowman and Penny make their way back, to meet on stage

It's hopeless, Penny—she's not out there. That means there's only one place she can be.
Penny Where?
Snowman Inside your house somewhere.

The tabs start to open

Penny (*leading the way through them*) Then let's go in and see.

SCENE 2

Penny's room. Immediately following

The window, now showing its interior side, is in the back wall, the Christmas tree, without the fairy, before it. Under it, on the floor, lies the fairy's wand. There is a fireplace, and from its mantel hangs an empty stocking. On the mantel, prominent among other ornaments, is a Nodding Mandarin. Furniture includes an armchair, a settee and Penny's bed, all suitable for a girl's room. It is a very untidy room. Penny's various belongings—polo-necks, jeans, a stocking, towels, shorts, skirts, dresses—are just dropped anywhere. A wellington boot stands on a chair. Comics, a hockey-stick, and other possessions lie around. There is an electric fire, which is switched on

Snowman Phew! What an H-E-A-T! I must get out again. (*He turns to go*)
Penny No—please don't go. I'll put the fire out. (*She switches it off*)
Snowman (*returning cautiously*) It's still there.

Penny What is?

Snowman The F-I-R-E. You said you'd put it out.

Penny So I have. I switched it off.

Snowman That's not the same thing, is it? If it were out, I wouldn't see it, would I? Because I would be in and it would be out. But *it*'s in and *I*'m not out, so . . .

Penny Oh, please don't be so difficult! It's just not ho . . . er, H-O-T any more.

Snowman (*circling cautiously into the room*) Mmmm—I don't know if I like it. Snowmen can't ever trust these things. (*Surveying the room*) Nor do I particularly care about all this. What a mess your room's in, girl!

Penny What's wrong with it?

Snowman It's in a kerfuffle!

Penny Oh, you sound just like Mum. That's what she says.

Snowman Well, isn't it? Just look at it. How could we possibly find any-thing—er—anyone in here?

Penny (*espying the wand*) I've found something. The wand! (*She picks it up*)

Snowman Oh good! Then the Fairy must be here, too, somewhere.

They look around, lifting various articles without actually displacing them

No—it's hopeless. She could be anywhere! We'll never find her in all this kerfuffle!

Penny All right, all right—don't go on about it! You're getting to sound more like Mum every minute.

Snowman You could, of course, try tidying up your room.

Penny Oh, that's a drag!

Snowman It needn't be. You have the wand.

Penny Y-e-s—so I have. Now we'll find out if she's a real fairy or not! If she is, this wand will be magic, won't it?

Penny tentatively points the wand at a garment on the chair or settee. The wardrobe door flies open of its own accord and the garment slides off, runs across the floor, and hangs itself up in the wardrobe. The wardrobe door closes

(*Open-mouthed*) Did you see that? It put itself away!

She repeats the action on another item—and another, and another, until she is dancing round the room touching everything lying about. One after another, they put themselves away. Now and again, if possible, the Snowman has to jump out of the way. The final object is the wellington boot standing alone on a chair. It does not immediately respond to the wand

Oh dear, the magic's running out!

Snowman Maybe it's too heavy.

Penny The wand?

Snowman No—the boot.

Penny The other one moved. (*She waves the wand again*)

The boot falls on one side. Penny stands beside it and stamps her feet quickly as if shooing an animal away. The boot falls off the chair. In a series of little stampings, Penny chases it, in spurts, until it disappears into the bottom of, or upstage of, the wardrobe. The wardrobe door closes

Snowman There! That looks much better!

Penny (*sitting on the settee*) I hardly know the place. My room—it's just too tidy for words! I'll never be able to find anything.

SONG—IF YOU WANT TO FIND A THING

The Snowman puts his foot on the end of the settee, leaning towards Penny with an admonishing finger

Snowman (*singing*)
    If you want
    To find a thing,
    You must always be
    In a state of excellence
    Where all is orderly!

During the three following verses the Snowman plays directly to the audience, even singling out individuals

    You can't hope
    To find your scarf
    To face the frosty air.
    If you've now forgotten how
    You've dropped it anywhere!

    When you want
    To go outside
    To play with your new ball,
    You need to know if it's in here,
    The kitchen, or the hall!

    How can you
    Expect to find
    Your shoes, your toes to toast,
    If one was left beneath a chair—
    The other you've just lost?

For the final verse, he returns to a sitting poition near Penny

    Take my tip
    And always put
    Things where they ought to be;
    Then, whate'er you're looking for,
    You'll find quite easily!

Penny Then where's the Fairy?

Snowman I beg your pardon?

Penny I didn't put her anywhere.

Snowman Oh. But you wished here in here—with the tree—didn't you?

Penny Well, she's not here, is she?

Snowman N-no. Unless she got lost in the kerfuffle!

Penny (*leaving the wand on the arm of the settee and wandering impatiently to the fireplace*) Oh, you *are* fond of that word, aren't you?

Snowman Of course I am. It's a very descriptive word. It fitted the situation exactly.

Penny (*addressing the mandarin on the mantelpiece*) *You* don't think she was lost in the kerfuffle, do you? (*She taps the mandarin's head lightly and, of course, it nods*) Oh—you!

Snowman (*rising*) What's that?

Penny A mandarin. But he says "yes" to everything.

Snowman He does?

Penny He's a Nodding Mandarin.

Snowman Is he really? That's very interesting. I wonder . . .? (*He goes to the fireplace*) Tell me, Mister Mandarin—am I to get my wish—the wish I wished me from the Fairy? (*He taps the mandarin's head lightly. The mandarin nods*) Oh, that *is* nice! That'll be something to look forward to.

Penny What will?

Snowman The wish I wished for myself—from the Fairy—before you came along and spoiled everything.

Penny Well, I like that! Whose Fairy is it, anyway?

Snowman Ah, but you see—I believe in fairies!

Penny (*impatiently*) Oh . . .! (*Looking round the room*) W-e-l-l—her wand *did* tidy up my room. (*Almost as if she might be beginning to believe*) What was it you wished for?

Snowman I'm not going to tell you.

Penny Oh—please!

Snowman I'm shy!

Penny (*laughing*) A shy snowman? (*Moving to him*) Go on—tell me.

Snowman I can't, anyway. It's a secret—between me and the Fairy.

Penny I won't tell.

Snowman You won't?

Penny Cross my heart and hope to die! (*She goes through the motions*)

Snowman (*wistfully*) Yes—that's just it. *I* don't!

Penny What?

Snowman Hope to die. You know, when you stop to think about it, it's not easy, being a snowman. It's very sad, in fact. One day you're here, and the next . . .?

Penny What *did* you wish for—Mr Fotheringay?

Snowman You remembered my name!

Penny Of course I did—er—do! It's not every snowman that . . .

Snowman. You *remembered*—my *name*! How nice! Nice—not to be forgotten. Perhaps you'll remember me too, afterwards . . .

Penny Afterwards?

Snowman When I'm a flower. (*He gasps, and puts his hand quickly over his mouth*)

Penny What's the matter?

Snowman I've gone and told you my wish!

Penny So what's wrong in that?

Snowman Er—nothing—I hope! (*He paces around desperately, looking for the Fairy*) Except that one should never tell a secret.

Penny I'll keep it.

Snowman (*still searching*) That's all very well—but will the Fairy—now?

Penny What are you looking for?

Snowman The Fairy. I must find her.

Penny Oh, she'll keep it. I'm sure she will.

Snowman What?

Penny Your secret.

Snowman Oh, it's not that. Fairies don't tell.

Penny Then what's wrong?

Snowman How do I know I haven't gone and broken the spell—by telling you?

Penny Y-e-s—I see what you mean. Wishes really are very private, aren't they?

Snowman So I must find her. (*His search is becoming very dispirited. He stops*) Wait a minute! You asked the mandarin.

Penny I did?

Snowman Yes. You said "she wasn't in the kerfuffle, was she?"

Penny So?

Snowman And the mandarin said "yes". Look! (*He goes to the fireplace*) Tell me, please, Mister Mandarin—was the Fairy lost in the kerfuffle? (*The mandarin, of course, responds to the Snowman's light tap by nodding*) You see? She *was* there—somewhere.

Penny Where?

Snowman In the kerfuffle!

Penny (*glancing round*) But there isn't any kerfuffle—now.

Snowman (*pondering this*) N-no—not now—but where does a kerfuffle go, when there isn't a kerfuffle any more?

Penny (*helpfully*) In the wardrobe?

Snowman No. When everything's been put away neat and tidy, it's not in a kerfuffle, is it?

Penny Er—no.

Snowman (*suddenly*) Where's the wand?

Penny (*indicating*) There.

The Snowman lifts the wand and holds it up before him, almost prayer-like

Snowman Oh, I do hope you've got your strength back. Please be strong!

Penny What are you going to do? (*She moves to the Snowman*)

Snowman (*to Penny*) Do you believe in fairies now? I mean—*really* believe?

Penny (*dithering*) Well—perhaps I do—a little . . .

Snowman (*to the audience*) Do you believe in fairies? 'Cos if you don't, it's time you got started! For I'm going to magic me a spell this time— such a spell as never was! Ready? I wish—I wish—I WISH TO BE IN AN AWFUL KERFUFFLE!

The following effects and entrances happen instantly and simultaneously

A deep gong sounds, followed by a cacophony of weird sounds, whistles, rocket-like swishes and exciting music. The Lighting goes haywire, with rapid changes of colour and flashes—the lights on the tree going quickly on and off. If possible, some of the furniture moves about

> *A Crocodile crawls across the stage. Mrs Penguin, carrying a shopping-basket, enters from the opposite side, crosses over and goes off. A Cockatoo enters and perches on the arm of the settee, where it sways from one foot to the other, screeching "Down with everything!"*

Penny and the Snowman dash about, bewildered, and everything works to a crescendo, as—

the CURTAIN *falls*

ACT II

Scene 1

A river bank. Immediately following

A rostrum runs across the back of the stage, with wide steps leading down from it. The whole is covered by grass matting or painted hessian to simulate a raised bank. One end is masked by a high hedge, the other by a bush. To one side of the stage is a large log; a small slate and a piece of chalk are hidden behind it

On the river bank, slightly nearer the bush than the hedge, with his back to the audience, stands the Fish. He wears a top-hat and is fishing, casting his line every now and then. He has nothing to say and takes not the slightest notice of anything going on. Until his exit he does not move from his position —for the simple reason that, if he did, he would lose his hat. Seated on the log is the Doctor-in-Law, hands on knees, watching all with interest. He is brightly dressed in coloured tail-coat, knee-breeches, long stockings and buckled shoes. His top-hat is enormous—capable, later, of coming down over Penny's head. He has a large, semi-stiff collar, the wings of which spread outwards, and either a brightly coloured cravat or a huge bow-tie. On his wrist he wears a large, brightly coloured watch—or even an alarm-clock

The Snowman and Penny are dashing about as at the end of Act I. In her hand, crumpled and unnoticeable Penny has a piece of paper about the size of a Treasury Note. The Cockatoo enters and perches on the hedge-end, shouting "Down with everything!" ad lib. Mrs Penguin, with her shopping-basket, crosses the stage and goes off, as before, the Crocodile enters to crawl behind the log so that, when hidden, his head is towards the centre of the stage. All the above happens simultaneously. As the effects finish, the Lighting resolves itself into a kind of daylight

Penguin (*as she passes the Cockatoo*) Good morning!
Cockatoo And down with you, too! (*Her agitation dies down with the rest of the effects*)

When all is normal, the Snowman and Penny gaze about them, bewildered, Each is backing slowly, Penny towards the log and the Snowman towards the Cockatoo. Silence.

Penny Now look what you've done! Where are we?

To a hint of Eastern music, the Mandarin enters, nodding, hands in sleeves, and with tiny steps but not quite running

Excuse me—can you tell us where we are?
Mandarin Yes, please. Thank you velly much.

The Manadarin trots off

Penny Well, that was very helpful!

The Cockatoo on the hedge gives a shrill whistle

Snowman (*below the end of the hedge, turning mildly*) Er—yes?

The Cockatoo screeches down at the Snowman and flaps his wings

Snowman (*moving swiftly away*) Oh, my goodness!

Penny has not yet noticed the Doctor-in-Law, who now rises, but the Snowman sees him dodging behind Penny, keeping out of her sight

Er—perhaps you can help us . . .

Penny turns to look behind her, but the Doctor-in-Law is too quick. She does not see him. She turns back to the Snowman

Penny Me?
Snowman No.
Penny Who?
Snowman Him.
Penny (*turning again*) I don't see anyone.
Snowman He's behind you.
Penny (*circling*) Who?
Snowman Him.

Penny advances on the Snowman, arms akimbo, the Doctor-in-Law following her step by step

Penny Are you trying to be funny?
Snowman (*again backing towards the Cockatoo*) Er—no—he's—er . . .
Penny If you say, once again, that he's behind me, I'll . . .
Snowman All right, all right! I'm seeing things!

The Cockatoo whistles

Snowman (*turning*) Er—yes?

The Cockatoo screeches down at Snowman and flaps his wings

Snowman (*starting*) Don't *do* that! Oh dear—I think I must go and lie
   down. All this is too much for me.
Penny I think perhaps it is.
Snowman It must be the H-E-A-T! There's no snow here—no ice—or
   anything nice—no cold winds—no biting frost—nothing! (*Making for
   the exit*) I must go and lie in the shade.

The Snowman exits

Penny (*facing front, only half speaking to the Snowman*) I think you'd
   better . . . (*In sudden panic*) No—don't go! You've got the wand—and
   we're lost! Come back! Come . . .

Penny is about to follow the Snowman, but the Doctor-in-Law removes his

hat and drops it over her head. It completely blinds her, and he spins her
round and round as if in preparation for a game of blind-man's-buff

Hey! What's going on? Stop it—stop . . .

The Cockatoo falls asleep. The Doctor-in-Law recovers his hat and replaces
it on his head

Doctor Certainly, my dear—certainly. (*He holds out his hand*) That'll be
twelve-and-a-half pence, please.
Penny What for?
Doctor Preventing you from getting lost. (*He leads her downstage*) You
were about to dash into the woods, where undoubtedly you would have
lost your way.
Penny But I have! I don't know where I am.
Doctor Oh, tut, tut! You should never say you don't know anything.
Even if you don't, you should always pretend that you do. That's *my*
regular dodge, and I ought to know. I'm a Doctor-in-Law.
Penny Well, where am I? And I'm afraid I don't know what a Doctor-in-
Law is, either.
Doctor One question at a time, my child. First of all, you are in the Land
of Kerfuffle. And as for being a Doctor-in-Law, that's a cross between
a father-in-law and a stepfather, with the doctor bit thrown in. A sort
of half-a-stepfather, in fact. And that'll be another twenty pence,
please. (*He holds out his hand*)
Penny What for?
Doctor Professional advice.
Penny I—I don't know what you mean.
Doctor Didn't I advise you never to say "I don't know"?
Penny But I didn't ask for your advice.
Doctor Oh, my dear—if I waited till people asked for advice, I should
never get any clients. And you might as well give me fifty pence for the
professional attendance. I always charge fifty pence for that.
Penny But I didn't want you to attend to me. And I wish you hadn't!
Doctor Ah, but that's just it. I should get no patients at all if I waited till
people wanted me to attend to them. So I always attend to them when
I think they require it—whether they wish me to or not. Now, I really
must insist on my fee, please. (*He produces a notebook, and a pencil stub,
which he licks*) Let me see, that'll be—er—three pounds, forty-two,
altogether, will it not?
Penny It certainly won't. How d'you make that out?
Doctor (*shrugging, expanding*) W-e-l-l, if you add all these charges to-
gether they come to—about that.
Penny They can't possibly!
Doctor (*in mock shock*) Oh, how very rude—contradicting your elders.
I'm surprised at you! Give me the money at once, please.
Penny (*getting a little alarmed*) But I—I haven't got any money.
Doctor No money? Oh dear me—this is serious, very serious. D'you

mean to tell me you're travelling around without any money in your pocket?

Penny I didn't know I was coming here—or that I should need any money. And besides, I haven't got a pocket.

Doctor Oh, that's an absurd excuse! What's that in your hand?

Penny opens her hand, and is surprised. She unfolds the Treasury Note and reads, astonished

Well?

Penny (*reading*) "Please Pay to Bearer the Sum of Five Kerfuffle Pounds. Signed, The Great Panjandrum."

Doctor How very fortunate—a Kerfuffle Order for Five Pounds! (*Quickly relieving her of it*) That will do very nicely. And now you will only owe me the odd fifteen pence.

Penny What odd fifteen pence? I don't remember anything about fifteen pence.

Doctor You don't?

Penny No, I don't!

Doctor How very odd!

Penny (*thinking she has at last got the better of him*) Yes, isn't it?

Doctor I'm so glad you agree.

Penny About what?

Doctor The fifteen pence being odd. But never mind—if you'll just give it to me . . .

Penny (*bewildered*) But I've already given you five pounds instead of three forty-two.

Doctor Oh, don't let that worry you. I'll overlook it this time. And if you haven't got the fifteen pence, I don't mind taking your watch instead. It looks a very nice watch.

Penny Y—you're horrible! And greedy!

Doctor Not at all, my dear. You're not looking at things in the right light. Don't you see—if you can't pay me the money, it's only fair that you should give me your watch.

Penny Allow me to tell you, Mr Doctor-in-Law, my watch is worth a great deal more than fifteen pence.

Doctor It can't possibly be. It's not nearly as big as mine—and mine only cost me five new pence.

Penny I'm not surprised. It doesn't even go. Mine does.

Doctor Does what?

Penny Go.

Doctor It does? Oh. In that case I don't want it. Who wants a watch that will go? A watch should stay. Why, if my watch was to go, I'd have to go after it, wouldn't I? To get it back again! (*He starts to go*) And now I must be off, or I shall be late for the Great Panjandrum. You can give me that other pound you owe me when we meet again.

Penny (*astounded*) What other pound? (*Panicking*) Oh, no—please! Don't go! Can you tell me . . . (*She follows him*)

Doctor Sorry. Can't stop. My time is far too valuable. (*At the exit*) And besides, you've got no money!

The Doctor-in-Law exits

Penny Oh dear, I hope everyone here is not like that.

THE SEALS' SONG

As the music starts the three Seals, dressed in tiny aprons and small poke-bonnets, dance—side-stepping arm-in-arm—across the stage in time to the words of the ditty. On the musical repetition of the fourth line they reverse direction, then, with the fifth line, reverse again and go off

Seals (*singing*)
    Ring-a-ding ding,
    We dance and we sing,
    For we are on holiday!
    Our teacher has got the mumps, so we
    Are going out to play!

The Seals exit

During the song, Penny backs towards the Cockatoo in amazement. After the Seals have gone, the Cockatoo whistles

Penny (*turning*) Yes?

The Cockatoo screeches at her, flapping his wings

Penny, with a little scream, runs to sit on the log. The Cockatoo makes a noise that might be taken for a laugh, then settles down to sleep again

  I don't see what there is to laugh at. You frightened me!

During this, the Minstrel enters. He is grandly dressed in a costume which could be roughly Elizabethan. He carries a very long walking-stick, and under one arm a parchment scroll. When he walks he is over-full of elegance—like a top model displaying a gown—but he has an extraordinarily long nose, large ears and a simply huge behind.

Minstrel (*striking a pose*) I wouldn't!

Penny, surprised, looks round, the Minstrel struts before her, then turns

  Don't you think I look handsome?
Penny (*trying to suppress her laughter*) Well, I wouldn't say you were exactly—
Minstrel (*cutting in*) —anything other than beautiful? Of course you wouldn't. I am very beautiful. And I'm very important, too.
Penny You are?
Minstrel Oh, very superior indeed. I am Minstrel to the Panjandrum.

Penny Who's he?
Minstrel (*off-handedly*) Oh—a sort of king.
Penny (*rather impressed*) A—king!
Minstrel Yes. The Great Panjandrum of Kerfuffle.
Penny Oh, yes. The Great Panjandrum. That was printed on the money
  I gave to the . . .
Minstrel (*moving quickly towards Penny*) Money?
Penny Oh, I haven't got any—now.
Minstrel (*patronizingly*) Oh. You poor thing! *I* have lots of money. I'm
  enormously rich. And I'm going to marry the Great Panjandrum's
  niece. Aren't you impressed?
Penny (*not very*) Oh, er—yes.
Minstrel So I should hope. I'm a composer, too.
Penny Really? What do you compose?
Minstrel Draughts.

Penny is mystified

  You've heard, surely, of people who compose draughts?
Penny Oh—yes—of course. Chemists. Sleeping draughts. They put you
  to sleep.
Minstrel Mine don't. Mine keep you awake. That's why they're much
  better than anyone else's.
Penny Are they difficult to compose?
Minstrel Oh, terribly. It requires a great brain like mine to do it pro-
  perly. (*Unrolling his scroll*) Would you like to hear my latest composi-
  tion?
Penny Yes, please. (*She places her hands in her lap, prepared to listen*)

The Minstrel clears his throat loudly

Minstrel (*reading*)
      Won't you walk into my parlour, said the spider to the fly?
      How I wonder what you are, up above the world so high.
      I'm going a-milking, sir, she said,
      But when she got there, the poor dog was dead!
Penny But that's . . .
Minstrel (*indignantly*) Quiet—please!
  (*He reads*)
      Four-and-twenty blackbirds, baked in a pie,
      Gin a body kiss a body, need a body cry?
      Humpty-Dumpty sat on a wall,
      And if I don't hurt her, she'll do me no harm!
  There—isn't that lovely?
Penny It's absolute rubbish! Why it's just a lot of—separate lines from
  different nursery rhymes, all strung together. And they don't even make
  sense!
Minstrel Sense? Sense? Whoever heard of poetry making sense? Any
  knowledgeable person would know that there should never be any

sense in really good poetry. In fact, the less you are able to understand poetry, the better it is.

Penny But all those lines were written by other people—different people.

Minstrel Of course they were. That's what makes it a composition. It's composed of bits. But the great thing is, of course, to get it to rhyme.

Penny The last two lines didn't!

Minstrel The last two lines? (*He consults the scroll, reading*)

> Humpty-Dumpty sat on a wall,
> And if I don't hurt her, she'll do me no harm!

Penny You see?

Minstrel (*speaking quickly, staccato*) Ah—well—you see—now—but—er—the secret is that you have to pronounce "harm" as nearly like "wall" as you can. You often have to do that in poetry, you know. (*Off-handedly*) And besides, people pardon little slips of that kind in really clever persons like myself. Well, good-bye. (*He moves to go*) It's been nice having you look at me, and listen. You may have the honour of meeting me again some time.

Penny Oh, please—don't go away!

Minstrel I must. The Great Panjandrum will be eagerly awaiting my presence at the Palace.

Penny (*moving to the Minstrel*) But I want to ask you something first. Have you seen Mr Fotheringay—or the Fairy—or can you tell me how to get home?

Minstrel Really! The presumption!

Penny Please help me.

Minstrel I have never heard of *Mister* Fotheringay. All *my* friends have titles! And I can't tell you how to get home because I don't know where your home is, do I? And as for your—what-is-it-you-called-it—fairy? I've never even *heard* of such a thing, so I wouldn't know if I'd seen it, would I? Does that help you?

Penny That's a fat lot of use!

Minstrel Good. I make a point of never doing anything useful. I am purely ornamental.

The Minstrel exits

Penny (*wandering down stage*) Well . . .! I must say I don't much like being in Kerfuffle!

The Gardener enters, desultorily clipping the hedge. The Cockatoo wakes to eye the Gardener distrustfully, shifting from one foot to the other

No-one's any help at all. (*Looking after the Minstrel*) Fancy not knowing what a fairy is. Oh, if only I had her wand, I could wish me home again. (*She sees the Gardener*) I wonder if he knows anything. (*To the audience*) I wonder if he knows anything? But I doubt it. If he's anything like the Minstrel, I doubt if he'd even know the time. What time is it, anyway? It was night when I left home, but here . . .? (*She gasps*) I hope I haven't missed Christmas! (*She consults her watch, then holds it to her ear*) Oh dear—it's stopped. (*She moves to the Gardener*) Excuse me, can you tell me the time, please?

Gardener (*at the end of the hedge*) Oh, we ain't got no such thing here, miss.

Penny Such thing as what?

Gardener Time.

Penny But you must have!

Gardener Why? What would I do with it if I had it? Lots of people don't have time.

Penny Yes, but that's people in a hurry. You don't seem to be in a hurry.

Gardener Oh, that's not the reason we haven't got time. We've just lost ours. You've heard of time bein' lost, haven't you?

Penny Er—yes.

The Gardener sits on the river bank by the hedge, motioning Penny to join him. She does so, sitting beside him

Gardener Shall I tell you how we lost ours?

The Cockatoo eyes the Gardener not too happily

We'd been keeping good time here for a long while, when along comes this edicated party wot calls himself a Doctor-in-Law.

Penny I've met him.

Gardener Ooo, you don't want to do that, miss! He's a right nut, he is. He ses to me, he ses, "You don't keep time properly." "Oh," I ses, "wot do you mean?" I ses. "Well," he ses, "you don't beat him, do you?" "No," I ses. "Wot would I want to beat time for?" "Oh," he ses, "you must be very strict with your time," he ses. "It needs beatin'."

Penny What did he mean?

Gardener I don't rightly know, miss, and that's a fact. And some of us, the second under-gardener, the muck-spreader and me, we don't much hold wi' them new-fangled ideas; but the others wanted to try it, so we took to beatin' time, regular, and for a while time *did* go quicker—so quick, in fact, we couldn't keep up wi' him! And so, of course, we fell behind. You've heard of people bein' behind time, haven't you?

Penny Yes. Please go on.

Gardener Well, miss, after a bit, what with our not beatin' him any more 'cos we couldn't keep up wi' him, our time began to go slower again, and there came a day when he slowly passed away altogether. You've heard of passing time, haven't you? Well, ours passed away.

Penny Where to?

Gardener We never heard. 'Unted 'igh and low for him, we did, but we could never find time. So now we haven't got any time worth speakin' of.

The Cockatoo whistles

Gardener (*looking up*) Er—yes?

The Cockatoo screeches at the Gardener and flaps his wings, the Gardener rises and, with his shears, snips the air angrily at the Cockatoo

The Cockatoo exits

Why, you—bird, you! I'll have the feathers off ye! Dang me, if I don't!

The Gardener follows the Cockatoo off

Penny (*not too hopefully*) No—don't go away! He never gave me a chance, either, to ask about Mr Fotheringay or the Fairy. (*She sits on the log, facing front, elbows on knees, chin on hands, pondering*)

The Fish has a bite. Slowly, concentrating on his catch, he lowers his head out of his hat and then moves along the bank, reeling in. He backs down on to the stage, still reeling. What he has caught is a bowler-hat, or other form of incongruous-looking head-gear. He unhooks it from the line, looks at it, puts it on, and shoulders his fishing-rod. His movements at all times are smooth and unhurried, as suggestive as possible of a fish in movement

The Fish exits

Penny, who has seen nothing of the above, suddenly swings one leg over the log to sit astride it

I wish I'd followed Mr Fotheringay

Crocodile (*from behind the log*) I wish you had, too. Get your foot off my back!

Penny glances behind the log, then, with a little scream, rises and runs downstage. The Crocodile emerges, stands up on his hind legs and yawns, stretching his "arms"

Would you like some tea?

Penny Er—yes, please.

Crocodile Good. I feel like some tea. A picnic tea.

Penny That—sounds lovely.

Crocodile (*closely examining a spot well downstage to one side*) Y-e-s, I think we'll have it—here!

Penny (*approaching cautiously to look at the spot*) Why there?

Crocodile It's where I always have my tea.

Penny Oh. Are you a local resident, then?

Crocodile Certainly not. I'm a crocodile. Are you a Proper Noun?

Penny No. I'm a girl.

Crocodile What's your name?

Penny Penny.

Crocodile How d'you spell that?

Penny Capital P-e-n-n-y.

Crocodile Ah—a capital! That makes you a Proper Noun. What shall we have for tea? Eggs, perhaps?

Penny Yes, please.

Crocodile And some cake—and jam?

Penny I should like that very much, thank you.

Crocodile But wait a minute. I'd better write all that down in case I forget.

The Fish enters

The Crocodile begins to search behind the log. Penny watches the Crocodile and does not see the Fish, who goes direct to the rostrum

That's funny. I know I have it here somewhere. (*He continues searching*)

As the Fish nears the suspended hat, he takes off the one he caught earlier and which he has entered wearing. He flings it back into the river, then gently eases himself under the suspended hat

The Fish walks off again, wearing his own hat

Ah, here it is. (*He feels behind the log and produces the slate and chalk, with which he again joins Penny*) Now, what was I doing? Oh yes—taking note. (*He writes*) Thin bread and butter. Eggs—boiled, I suppose?

Penny nods

Crocodile (*still writing*) Tea—cake—jam. There! Are you sure you won't have anything else?
Penny That will do nicely, thank you.
Crocodile Good. (*He replaces the slate and chalk behind the log*) Right—where are the things?
Penny What things?
Crocodile Why, the things for tea, of course.
Penny I haven't got them. You asked me to have tea with you!
Crocodile (*sobbing*) I think that's very c-cruel of you! Raising my hopes l-like that and then—and then—disa . . . disa . . . disappointing me! (*He sits on the log and bawls. If possible he uses a clown's "eye-fountains"—a water-filled bulb in his pocket with thin rubber tubing under his costume and mask—so that jets of water spout from his eyes*)
Penny Oh, please don't cry.
Crocodile (*sobbing bitterly*) Y-you said we were going to have—t-tea—w-with—e-eggs—and—and—and cake—and—and . . . (*But he has forgotten. He immediately stops sobbing, rises briskly and goes behind the log, consults the slate, then returns and bawls again*) And J-J-A-A-M! (*He weeps copiously*)
Penny (*going to comfort him*) Poor Mr Crocodile!

THE SEALS' SONG (reprise)

The three Seals enter, dancing side by side, with "action" motions to suit their lines. They dance to the middle of the stage, with a reversal of direction on the fourth line, another reversal on the non-speaking bar eight of the music, then off again on the fifth line

Seals (*singing*)
    Rub-a-dub-dub!
    We scrub in a tub,
    For Monday is washing-day!
    On Tuesday we hang them out to dry.
    On Wednesday we go away!

The smallest Seal returns momentarily to announce to the audience

C

Seal We don't like doing the ironing, that's why! (*She claps her hands low, like the flippers of a seal, clapping with the backs of her hands to give a more seal-like effect*)

The hand of another Seal appears and descends upon the first Seal's shoulder, then yanks her off, the first Seal giving a jump off sideways to give the impression that she has been lifted off bodily

Crocodile (*brightening*) I know what we'll do! Do you ever have tea for breakfast?

Penny Always. I don't like coffee.

Crocodile Then that's it. We'll have breakfast for tea instead.

Penny But how can we—if we haven't anything to eat?

Crocodile Oh, but I have all we need for breakfast. Between ourselves, have most of it hidden there—(*indicating*)—behind the log. There's bread—butter—two eggs—some cake—and a pot of lovely, lovely jam

Penny But that's exactly what we were going to have for tea!

Crocodile Not quite, my dear. I said *most* of it was there.

Penny Then what else is there?

Crocodile You.

Penny (*beginning to back, circling to behind the log*) M-me?

Crocodile (*circling slowly after her, menacingly*) Oh, I always have little girls for breakfast!

The three Seals enter, dancing across the stage, then back to the middle

THE SEALS' SONG (reprise)

Seals (*singing*)
> Rat-a-tat-tat!
> We sit and we chat,
> Each afternoon at three,
> With chocolate cakes and cream meringues,
> And crocodiles for tea!

The Crocodile is now behind the log, towering over Penny, who has been forced to sit on it, with her back to the audience. The Crocodile's arms are raised in menace, but this leaves him immediately when he realizes what the Seals have just said. His arms drop

Crocodile (*unbelievingly*) Crocodiles for tea?

The Seals all repeat the last line of their song, during which they dance across to group closely in front of Penny, thus blocking her entirely from view

Seals (*singing*)
> Crocodiles for tea!

Crocodile (*more loudly, moving away*) Croc-odiles for t-e-a?

First Seal In the sandwiches, dear.

Crocodile But I don't want to be a s-s-sandwich!

Second Seal Then, afterwards, you'd make a lovely pair of shoes.

Third Seal Or a handbag.

Crocodile (*à la Dame Edith Evans*) A h-a-n-d-b-a-g?

Penny slips down behind the log, out of sight

First Seal Oh, crocodile handbags are all the rage.
Second Seal Yes. Very fashionable.
Third Seal And you'd make a lovely one.
Crocodile I don't want to be anybody's h-handb-bag!
First Seal (*moving to one side of the Crocodile*) Oh, please—just a little one!
Second Seal (*moving to the Crocodile's other side*) Three little ones—one each!
Third Seal (*moving beside the First Seal*) If you eat up your breakfast nicely, you could just about stretch to that.
Crocodile (*looking towards the log*) It's gone!
First Seal What has?
Crocodile My breakfast!
Third Seal (*moving slightly away, in mock comfort*) Why so she has. What a shame!
Crocodile Not that I feel like any breakfast now. All this talk of shoes and handbags has put me right off it.
Second Seal And sandwiches. Don't forget the sandwiches.
Crocodile (*backing away*) I don't think you're being very n-nice to me! You've no idea how sad it is, being a crocodile—and being made into—shoes—and handbags—and—and s-sandwiches!

The Crocodile exits, bawling

THE SEALS' SONG (reprise)

Seals (*dancing in unison downstage*)
    Rub-a-dub-dub,
    Three seals in a tub
    Went fishing on the Nile,
    But all they caught was a Green Line bus
    And a poor old Crocodile!

Penny peeps up from behind the log

Penny Has he gone?
First Seal Who?
Penny Jaws.
First Seal Yes.
Penny (*rising*) Thank goodness! I didn't much like the idea of being his breakfast! (*She joins the Seals downstage*)
First Seal That would have been quite the wrong kind of surprise.

The front tabs close

The Seals' Rookery. The action is continuous

Second Seal For breakfast, anyway.

Penny For any time.

First Seal But especially breakfast. That's quite the nicest time for sur-
prises.

Penny Is it?

Second Seal Of course it is. That's when the postman comes.

First Seal Which reminds me. There's a letter for you.

Penny How do you know?

First Seal Because I wrote it. (*She produces an envelope*) I've got it for you
here.

Penny (*reading*) "Miss Penny, care of the Crocodile, the Land of Kerfuffle." Oh—perhaps it's from Mr Fotheringay—or the Fairy. (*She
extracts the letter*) Why, what's this? (*She turns it over, but the reverse
is obviously blank*)

First Seal Wasn't it kind of me to send it?

Penny (*looking in the envelope*) But there's nothing in it.

First Seal Isn't there a letter?

Penny No. (*She displays the communication*) Nothing but a plain sheet of
paper with a large "C" on it.

First Seal Well, that's a letter, isn't it? I didn't say I'd sent you a lot of
letters—only one! How many did you expect? And I thought you'd like
the letter "C".

Penny What for?

First Seal To suggest things. You've only got to look at it to think of all
kinds of lovely things that begin with "C"—like—cake and—cream and
—chocolate—and candy—and crumpets . . .

Second Seal To say nothing of carpets and clowns and coral necklaces!

Third Seal Of course, there are *some* uncomfortable things that begin
with "C"—like caterpillars and—castor-oil and—crocodiles! But on the
whole, it's a very good letter.

First Seal Yes—a lot different from some I could name.

Second Seal I had the letter "M" sent to me once, and I immediately got
the mumps and the measles.

Third Seal She didn't really get better until I'd sent her a "G" for grapes.

Penny (*entering into the spirit of the game*) Oh—I get the idea. Why
didn't you send her an "F" for fruit? That would have given her lots of
things.

Second Seal Yes—like frogs and freckles and five-finger exercises! No
thank you!

A deep gong sounds three times

Penny What's that?
First Seal The call to the daily conference—with the Great Panjandrum.

The front tabs begin to open

  Everyone goes to the conference

SCENE 3

The Panjandrum's Palace. The action is continuous

The hedge, bush, grass matting and log have been struck from the river bank setting. In the centre of the rostrum is a throne, just a little too high and too wide for the Panjandrum, when he enters, to sit on comfortably. Five stools or seats are ranged on either side of the stage—one of those nearest to the rostrum being a high-backed chair or thronelet. This is the Fish's seat. (The Grand Hall can be elaborated with the addition of pillars, a carpet leading up to the throne, statues, a chandelier, etc., to the director's taste)

When all are present, their positions are:

                    Panjandrum (*on the throne*)
(*On the rostrum edge*) Cockatoo   Doctor (*standing beside the throne*)
            Fish   Mandarin
        Crocodile   First Seal
        Gardener   Second Seal
    Mrs Penguin   Third Seal
Penny   Minstrel

As the tabs open, the Fish is already seated, quietly reading a comic—he remains in his seat until the end of the scene. The Crocodile and the Gardener have almost reached their places. The three Seals dance through the tabs to their places, singing as they go

THE SEALS' SONG (reprise)

Seals (*singing*)
    Ting-a-ling-ling!
    We haven't a thing
    To worry about today!
    We're stringing along to join the throng,
    To hear what they have to say.

They reach their positions

  Mrs Penguin and the Cockatoo enter, each from the side opposite to their seats

They are about to cross each other when Cockatoo stops and sways, bird-

like, from side to side. Mrs Penguin tries to get past, first one way, then the other. Eventually she decides to remain on the side from which she entered. The Cockatoo whistles

Mrs Penguin (*turning*) Yes?

The Cockatoo screeches and flaps his wings

(*Flouncing*) Oh! (*She waddles to her seat*)

The Cockatoo turns, swaying. The Seals begin to sway in unison. The swaying becomes more pronounced—as if the Cockatoo and the Seals were in competition. A fanfare sounds. The Cockatoo goes to his place on the rostrum and jumps up and down on the edge, screeching

All (*except* **Penny**)
    The Panjandrum!
    The Great Panjandrum!
    Here he comes!   }(*Speaking together* ad lib.)
    He's coming! He's coming!

The Royal procession enters, to music, led by the Doctor-in-Law, who carries a gavel. He is followed by the Panjandrum, small and fat, wearing clothes, robe and crown which are much too big for him. His crown has slipped down over one eye, making it difficult for him to see where he is going, and he keeps tripping on his robe. In place of an orb and sceptre he carries a brightly coloured ball and a ball-and-cup toy or a feather duster. He is followed by the Mandarin who is playing with a yo-yo, his head nodding in time to it. Lastly comes the Minstrel, complete with scroll

All except Penny take their places, the Minstrel first ensuring that he displays himself before everyone like a peacock. The Doctor-in-Law makes his way to the rostrum. The Panjandrum trips his way after, as he has been delayed by dipping curtsies to all and sundry on his way. When he reaches the throne he finds it too high to sit normally, so he lays his "orb" and "sceptre" on the rostrum and knees his way on to the throne like an infant on to a high chair. Then he finds he cannot reach his "orb" and "sceptre", and this worries him. His left arm is on the arm of the throne

Doctor (*over the hubbub*) Silence, please!

No-one pays any attention. The hubbub continues

(*Roaring*) QUIET!!

Sudden dead silence. The Doctor-in-Law glares round, then, as if to emphasize his authority, he bangs his gavel once on the arm of the throne— where the Panjandrum has his fingers

Panjandrum (*jumping from the throne and dancing in pain*) Ow! Ow-oh-ooooo!

The Doctor-in-Law prods the Panjandrum with the gavel and points him back to the throne: to speed his return he helps to push him on

Doctor (*in his normal voice, holding the gavel near the Panjandrum's face*)
Quiet!

Panjandrum Yes, your majesty.

*The Doctor-in-Law thrusts the "orb" and "sceptre" at the Panjandrum who,
not knowing quite what to do with them, pushes them to the back of his seat,
then proceeds to fall asleep*

Doctor (*giving light taps for attention generally*) Now . . . (*He sees Penny,
who is still downstage*) Who's that down there?

Penny It's—it's only me.

Doctor You're late!

Penny But I've not been here before.

Doctor Then if you're not before, you must be behind—and that's what I
said in the first place—you're late! Sit down! (*He indicates the vacant
seat*)

Penny sits

Mrs Penguin Are you a Proper Noun?

Penny No. Er—yes.

Mrs Penguin Good. All girls are nouns, you know. Although all nouns
are not girls—which is very peculiar, when you come to think about it.

Doctor Can we please have much hush.

Mrs Penguin Sorry.

Penny I hardly spoke.

Cockatoo Yes, she did! She's been talking ever since she came in.

Doctor Quiet—everybody! It's time for the speech from the throne. (*He
prods the dozing Panjandrum*) Now then, Panjandrum, sparkle up!

Panjandrum (*waking*) Eh? What? Oh—er—yes, your majesty. (*He slides
from the throne to stand before it*) May it please your majesties . . .

Minstrel (*rising and unrolling his scroll*) I will now oblige you with one of
my charming songs.

Cockatoo Oh no, you don't! Down with him! Down with him!

Crocodile ⎫ We don't want to hear it! We don't want to hear it! ⎫ (*Speaking
Gardener ⎬ Turn him out! Turn him out!   ⎬ together*)
Seals ⎭ Not if we can help it, you won't!   ⎭

Doctor (*using his gavel*) Will you all please be quiet! (*To the Panjandrum*)
Pray continue.

Panjandrum (*curtsying to the Doctor*) Yes, sir. (*Generally*) May it please
your majesties . . .

Cockatoo (*edging slightly in along the rostrum*) What about me, eh? What
about me?

Panjandrum And—and you, your majesty.

Minstrel We don't want to listen to all this rubbish!

Doctor (*to the Panjandrum*) He's quite right, you know. You're very bor-
ing. Sit down.

Panjandrum (*meekly*) Yes, sir. (*He climbs on the throne and sits, fidgeting*)

The Cockatoo edges back to his former position

Mrs Penguin What about questions and answers? I like questions and
answers.
Doctor (*looking around*) Has anyone got a question?
Mrs Penguin (*rising*) I have. (*She recites*)
>The people of Japan, I've heard,
>Are really most polite;
>To compliment all sorts of things
>Is daily their delight.
>
>They speak in terms of courtesy
>Of an "honourable" table,
>And flatter other household things
>Whenever they are able.
>
>Determined not to be outdone
>In manners so genteel,
>I now express to all my goods
>The deep respect I feel.
>
>But the system I've adopted
>Is really most confusing,
>And circumstances oft arise
>Which are not at all amusing.
>
>For on my most distinguished table
>Was a well-connected dish,
>And reposing gently on it
>Was an influential fish.
>
>But my honourable cat, I fear,
>Was unfortunately there,
>And very quickly sprang up
>On my estimable chair.
>
>When seeking, somewhat later,
>For my influential fish,
>I discovered not a particle
>On my well-connected dish.
>
>The question now arises,
>And I think I ought to know,
>How far this fulsome flattery
>Expects a bird to go.
>
>Am I compelled by etiquette—
>Now, please to tell me that—
>To call a cat that steals my fish
>An honourable cat?

Doctor (*looking around enquiringly, then using his gavel*) Grannie, stir the pot!

Immediately there is a mad dash and much confusion as everyone changes places to—

Panjandrum
      Mandarin   Doctor
   Fish   Gardener
  Third Seal   Crocodile
 First Seal   (Empty seat)
Second Seal   (Empty seat)
Minstrel   Cockatoo

Mrs Penguin retains her position. Penny, pushed from her seat by the Minstrel, stands at a loss

Penny (*to Mrs Penguin*) What's going on?
Mrs Penguin We have to change our positions, dear, so that we can hear both sides of the question. You can sit over there. (*She indicates the seat next to the Crocodile*)

Penny sits

Doctor Silence, please! Now repeat the question.
Mrs Penguin (*reciting*)
    Am I compelled by etiquette,
    Now, please to tell me that,
    To call a cat that steals my fish
    An honourable cat?
Doctor Well, what's the verdict?
Cockatoo I should like to ask a few questions before replying.
Mrs Penguin Certainly.
Cockatoo You said you'd "heard" that the people of Japan were polite. Where did you hear it?
Mrs Penguin I read it in a book.
Cockatoo Ah! Did you hear that, everyone? She's lying. She didn't hear it at all. She read it in a book—and that's not the same thing. (*To Mrs Penguin*) Tell me, has your cat left?
Mrs Penguin Er—no
Cockatoo Then if it's not left, it must be right. Which means that, in future, you must call her the *right* honourable!

General agreement. Mrs Penguin, not very pleased, sits beside the Cockatoo, whom she eyes with suspicion. The Panjandrum fiddles with the knees of his breeches

Doctor (*slapping the Panjandrum's hand away*) Stop fidgetting! What's wrong with you? Got woollies on?

The Panjandrum cowers

    (*Generally*) Any more questions?

The Panjandrum raises his arm and snaps his fingers, but no-one takes the slightest notice

Minstrel I have. It's in French. (*In a superior tone*) Although I doubt if anyone here knows how to speak French.
Penny I do—a little.
Minstrel (*patronizingly*) Really?
Cockatoo Down with foreigners! Down with foreigners!
Doctor Silence! Proceed.
Minstrel Has the son of the miller got the mustard of the daughter of the gardener?
Penny That's not French!
Minstrel Of course it is. (*To the Doctor, anxiously*) Isn't it?
Doctor Well, I—er—I have seen questions very much like that in my French lesson book.
Minstrel (*to Penny*) You see? It must be French!
Cockatoo (*to Penny*) Yah! Who said she knew French and didn't? (*To all and sundry*) Laugh at her! Laugh at her!
Doctor (*commandingly*) Grannie, stir the pot!

General confusion, as everyone changes back to their original positions

Well, does anyone know the answer?
Gardener I can tell ye.
Doctor Then, has he?
Gardener Yes.
Doctor How do you know?
Gardener He told me.
Doctor Ah. Then that's it. Next question.

The Panjandrum raises his arm as before, but still no-one notices. The Mandarin's music is heard as he rises

Mandarin (*rising*) Yes, please. (*He proceeds, nodding, to sit cross-legged on the middle of the floor, facing the audience*)
First Seal He's getting married, you know.
Second Seal To Dinah.
Third Seal From China.
Doctor Is he?
Mandarin Oh, it's sad when you cannot say "No",
And your head on a pivot is fixed.
If one has to consent
When a negative's meant,
One's affair's get so hopelessly mixed!

The First Seal sits beside the Mandarin

First Seal And that is the Mandarin's case,
Of that there cannot be doubt.
She asked him to wed
And he nodded his head,
And that's how it all came about.

Mandarin   It happened one day in the spling,
            As I sat 'neath my led palasol.
            Though she looked velly meek,
            She did have a cheek—
            She was only a black lubber doll!

The Second Seal sits on the Mandarin's other side

Second Seal I think it was dreadfully mean,
            For she knew that he couldn't refuse;
            He had to say "Yes"
            Though he rues it, I guess.
            Aren't you glad that you're not in his shoes?
Mandarin   She must be a stlong-minded girl,
            For they say she has pulchased the ling,
            And threatens, I've heard,
            If I go from my word,
            To dlag me to church with a stling!

The Third Seal goes to kneel behind the Mandarin

Third Seal They say she's a terrible shrew
            And will lead him a regular dance;
            And although she's so plain,
            She's remarkably vain—
            And *will* have her dresses from France!
Mandarin   She asks me for this thing and that—
            No wonder I'm tellibly vexed!
            I keep nodding my head,
            Although tlembling with dlead,
            For I never know what she'll want next!
Seals   The only thing we can suggest,
            Is to ask him some day to agree
            To execute Dinah,
            Or send her to China—
            He's bound to consent, don't you see?

There is a general nodding of heads

Doctor Agreed.

The Mandarin and the Seals resume their former positions

Minstrel (*taking the stage*) You will all be delighted to hear that I am now going to sing.
All (*ad lib.*) No. Put him out! Oh no, you don't. Down with him! Not if we can help it! etc.

The Minstrel, put out, resumes his seat. The Panjandrum is fidgetting terribly, and holding up his hand

Doctor Don't jiffle about like that. What's wrong with you?

Panjandrum I'm afraid, your majesty, that I shall have to present another petition.

Doctor Again? What do you want know? You're always wanting something. Last week it was to have your shoes repaired, the week before, you wanted your hair cut. Now you want something else!

Panjandrum No, your majesty, it's the same thing.

Doctor The same as what?

Panjandrum Before.

Doctor Your shoes? Again?

Panjandrum No, your majesty—my hair. If you remember, you couldn't all agree last time as to whether I might have it cut or not.

Doctor That's right. We were equally divided on the issue.

Panjandrum So, to please everybody, I only had it half cut. May I now please humbly beg to have the rest taken off?

The crowd murmurs

Gardener Let's have a look at ye, with your crown off.

The crowd agrees. "Take off your crown", etc. The Panjandrum removes his crown to reveal one side of his head almost completely shorn, while the other is long, dishevelled hair

Doctor (*considering it*) Yes, I suppose it does look rather silly. How much will it cost to have it cut?

Panjandrum Two-and-a-half pence.

Cockatoo Too much! Down with Panjandrums! Down with barbers! Down with everybody!

Doctor Hold your tongue! (*Generally*) Well—what shall we say to the Panjandrum's petiton?

There is a general murmur

Minstrel (*rising and topping the hubbub*) To any *intelligent* person, the answer is very simple. We merely have to wait until the short hair is as long as the long hair, then he can have it all off at once.

Doctor Agreed. (*He takes the crown from the Panjandrum and slaps it down on the Panjandrum's head*)

The Panjandrum returns to sulking

Any other business?

Penny Can I say something, please?

Doctor Pray do.

Penny I—I think you're all being very mean—to the poor Panjandrum.

Cockatoo Never mind all that rubbish. Get on with it!

Doctor Yes, the matter is closed. Have you a question?

Penny W-well, yes. I'd like to know what's happened to the Snowman— and the Fairy.

Cockatoo Unfair! That's two questions. Unfair!

Doctor He's right, you know. We can only deal with one question at a time.

Penny All right. Where's Mr Fotheringay? He's my friend.

Mrs Penguin Where would he normally be, dear?

Penny In the garden, of course.

Gardener She be right, too. That's where all respectable snowmen should be.

Doctor Did you turn him out of the garden, or not?

Penny Not.

Minstrel Did a dog chase him away?

Penny No.

Doctor Then, there you are. Two negatives. You said "not" and "no". If you have two negatives together, that means "yes"—so he must be in your garden.

Penny Y-you're confusing me!

Mrs Penguin You're confusing yourself, my dear. If you say you have not no snowman in your garden, that means you have.

Cockatoo And you did!

Minstrel So you have!

Doctor There. That's the first question answered. Your snowman's in the garden. Now, what was the other thing you wanted to know, please?

Penny Well, I—I was asking what had happened to the Fairy . . .

There is a general reaction of puzzlement

   Haven't you ever heard of a fairy?

Doctor Er—f-fairy? How d'you spell it?

Penny F-a-i-r-y.

Everyone looks blank, some at each other, shrugging

Doctor What is it?

Penny Well, a fairy's a . . . Er—a fairy is . . .

Cockatoo Never heard of it!

Crocodile Is it for eating?

Penny No!

Minstrel Can you wear it?

Penny *No!*

Gardener It's not some new kind of spray, is it—for greenfly?

Penny NO!

Mrs Penguin Could it be a slot-machine, dear, where you put in a penny and get bubble-gum?

Penny *NO!* Oh, forget it. I'm sorry I asked.

Doctor What do you want this fairy for, anyway?

Penny Because she has a wand—a magic wand. And I need it!

Doctor Ah—that puts an entirely different light on the matter. You should frame your questions more carefully, my dear. It's not really a fairy we're looking for, is it? It's a wand.

The Minstrel suddenly starts waltzing in a corner, with his staff as a partner, singing to the tune of "German Band"

Minstrel (*singing*)

Has anyone seen the fairy's wand?
Magic wand?
In this land . . . ?

All Quiet—sit down. Silence! Oh, not you again!, etc.

Doctor (*using his gavel*) Order! Order!

Silence. Everyone waits. All are on the edges of their seats, awaiting an expected command

(*Suddenly*) Grannie, stir the pot!

There is a mad scramble to change seats, which this time are not prearranged, thus adding to the confusion. The Seals, however, are not far separated in their final positions

Well, does anyone know where we can find this wand?

All shake their heads except the Mandarin, who nods

Cockatoo I don't believe she knows, herself!

Doctor (*to Penny, alarmed*) Don't you?

Penny Well, I didn't know where Mr Fotheringay was, did I? You say he's in my garden, but he came here with me.

Doctor (*aghast*) You don't know where the wand is?

Penny No.

Doctor (*severely*) It's no good whatever asking questions if you don't know the answer yourself.

Penny (*puzzled*) Why not?

Doctor (*almost angrily*) Because if you don't know yourself, how can you tell whether or not we give you the right answer?

Minstrel Now we're for it!

Doctor (*like a teacher, punishing the whole class*) Right! You're still looking for a wand. And if you haven't found it by tomorrow, I'll—I'll make every one of you walk on the black lines of the pavement for the rest of the week!

General groans

Panjandrum (*with his arms raised, snapping his fingers*) Please—please . . .

Doctor Now what do you want?

Panjandrum Please, sir—I'm—I'm hungry, sir.

Doctor (*raising his arms for general attention*) Attention, everyone! The Great Panjandrum has invited us all to dinner.

Panjandrum (*jumping from his throne, panic-stricken*) No! No—you can't! The cook'll kill me—she doesn't like people coming for meals unexpected!

No-one pays any attention

THE SEALS' SONG (reprise)

Seals (*dancing and singing together*)
  Yum-a-yum-yum!
  Some food in our tum!
  We're all going off to dine
  On chips and beans and kidley-pie,
  Tomato sauce and wine!

Doctor (*gesturing magnificently off stage*) To the Dining-Hall!

Led by the Seals, all except Penny, the Gardener, the Fish and the Panjan-drum, join in a fantastic, conga-like dance and go off, repeating the Seals' chorus, then fading away

Panjandrum (*in utter confusion with his robe, crown, "orb" and "sceptre", following the others off*) Oh dear—I'll never be able to get another cook . . .

The Panjandrum exits

Gardener (*bringing his stool and setting it down near Penny*) Bound to be around somewhere, miss. Everything here's in a kerfuffle, you might say.

The Gardener exits

Penny (*sitting on the stool*) Oh dear—I wish I'd believed in fairies in the first place! Then all this might never have happened! (*She stares out front, chin on hand*)

The Fish, lowering his comic, realizes the others have gone. He rises, nose buried in the comic again, and slowly walks, still reading, after them. About half-way across he lowers his head to blow open the next page of the comic. This movement frees him from his hat

The Fish walks off, without his hat, reading

Penny, downstage of the Fish's line of travel, is unaware of all the above. The Lights fade on Penny, alone, with the hat in mid-air, as—

the CURTAIN *falls*

ACT III

SCENE 1

The river bank

The stage is empty except for the Cockatoo, who is perched on the hedge, half asleep. The Fish strolls along the raised bank from the opposite side, crossing at a leisurely pace. He is absorbed in a comic, which he carries in his upstage fin. With his downstage fin he drags behind him an empty shopping trolley. He does not halt at all, merely crosses the stage and disappears from view. His hat, however, is following him, gently undulating in the air at roughly head-level and about five or six feet behind him. About a yard before it reaches the hedge, the hat stops

On the Fish's entrance, the Cockatoo looks beadily around, then away again, not much interested. Then he "double-takes" on the floating hat. When the hat stops he eyes it, his head cocking at a variety of bird angles. He whistles. The hat's front brim tilts upwards, as if some invisible person wearing it had looked up at him. He screeches and flaps his wings

At lightning speed, the hat dashes off after the Fish. The Snowman peeps round the proscenium arch

Snowman Remember me? (*He steps forward*) Oh, lovely! Now, what did I tell you to say? Come on—surely you haven't forgotten? I said— (*He sings*)

THE SNOWMAN'S SONG (reprise)

When you meet me in the snow,
Don't forget to say "Hullo!"
Like a Christmas card,
It's not very hard
To spread a little, friendly glow!
So—(*loudly*)—HULLO!

The Gardener enters upstage, gathering weeds, which he drops into a basket he carries

(*Still speaking to the audience*) That's better! Know where I've been? (*He thumbs off*) Sleeping in a snowdrift! It's a fact. I just—conjured one up—with this—the Fairy's wand. (*He holds it up*) So now I'm nice and cold again. But where's Penny? It's her I'm looking for. And how long have I been asleep, anyway? Do you know, I don't even know if today's tomorrow or if it's still yesterday. I'd like someone to tell me.

Gardener (*moving to the Snowman*) Why—be you havin' trouble wi' your time as well, then?

Snowman You too?

Gardener Oh, we're terrible mixed up in Kerfuffle. Take now, for example.

Today, we're in the middle of next week, and tomorrow, like as not, it'll be the day before yesterday.

Snowman Oh. (*To the audience*) I can see he's not going to be very much help. (*He starts to move off*)

Gardener (*catching the Snowman by the arm*) It's the length of days here that confuse a body. Some days is that short, you can hardly get your clothes on before it's time to take 'em off again and go to bed. Then others is that long you're obliged to have eight or nine dinners a day or you'd starve!

Snowman (*uninterestedly*) Oh, yes?

Gardener And as for the days of the week, there's no dependin' on them. I've known thirteen Fridays in one week, which is most unlucky.

Snowman (*turning away again*) Never mind, it'll soon be Christmas.

Gardener (*again delaying the Snowman*) Ah—but that's just it! It might not be! Last year, Christmas was only two days after Easter, and then we 'ad three New Year's Days running.

Snowman How awkward for you. (*Suddenly interested*) Er—how d'you know when it's your birthday?

Gardener We don't. It's quite impossible to tell how old you are here. Take my son, Willie, now—he was born in March—and a little while ago it kept being March over and over again. He's had that many birthdays more than me, now, he must be a hundred, if he's a day!

Snowman Now you're getting *me* confused!

Gardener "Confused" ain't the word, sir. (*He pokes his face very close to the Snowman's*) Look at me daughter . . .

Snowman (*holding his head away*) I'd much rather—if she doesn't also eat onions!

Gardener She was to have been married on the nineteenth of June, but dang me if there's been a nineteenth of June in the last twenty years. Why, her husband-to-be-that-was is that old now, I reckon he's past it!

Snowman (*to the audience*) I can see I shall have to do something about him, or I'll never be rid of him.

The Snowman moves away, thinking, crossing the Gardener, who is now close to the proscenium arch

(*To the Gardener, over his shoulder*) Er—stay there a moment. I'm thinking. (*He sees the Cockatoo*)

Gardener Think ye can change things around here, then?

Snowman (*a great light dawning*) Ye-es—I think I just can. I wish—(*he points the wand at the Gardener*)—I wish—(*he points his wand at the Cockatoo, then, with the wand vertical, he looks upwards*)—you know what I'm wishing for! (*He closes his eyes, hunches his shoulders, and waits*)

The sound effects from the finale of Act I are repeated, coupled with the dipping of all Lights, several times, each dip greater than its predecessor, the final dip being a momentary Black-out

D

During the Black-out the Reserve Cockatoo and Reserve Gardener quickly change places with the Gardener and Cockatoo respectively

The Snowman opens his eyes. He is delighted. He approaches the Reserve Cockatoo—where the Gardener was—thumbing an indication to the Reserve Gardener on the hedge—where the Cockatoo was

That'll give him something to worry about—getting down off there!

The Reserve Cockatoo pokes his head forward and raises his wings menacingly

Oh—er—yes—I—er . . . (*He turns to exit, below the Reserve Gardener*) I think I'll go this-a-way!

The Reserve Gardener whistles like a Cockatoo as the Snowman is passing below

Snowman (*looking up*) Er—yes?

The Reserve Gardener screeches like the Cockatoo and flaps his arms

Snowman Oh, my goodness!

The Snowman exits quickly

The Reserve Cockatoo carries on with the weeding

Mrs Penguin enters from along the river bank, carrying a flag-tray gaily decorated with rosettes. On the tray are several small coloured jars and a number of flag-day-type flags. From the front of the tray there hangs a notice—EXCUSES. Mrs Penguin is about to proceed down off the bank when she sees the Reserve Gardener on the hedge

Mrs Penguin Whatever are you doing up there at your age?

The Reserve Gardener shifts from foot to foot, his arms flapping slightly

Have you found that wand yet—what everyone's looking for?

The Reserve Gardener sways like a Cockatoo

Oh, be like that, then! (*She flounces down off the bank*)

The Reserve Gardener whistles like the Cockatoo

Mrs Penguin (*turning*) Yes?

The Reserve Gardener screeches and flaps his arms. Mrs Penguin gives a little scream and runs down towards the Reserve Cockatoo

How you do frighten a woman! (*She looks at the Reserve Cockatoo*) I should have thought that one of you would be enough. (*She moves towards the Reserve Gardener again with a "shooing" motion*) You just get down off there, you silly old goat. Shoo! Shoo!

The Reserve Gardener disappears, squawking, behind the hedge. The Minstrel enters, carrying an open scroll and a quill. He reads out loud what he is in the middle of composing

Minstrel Little Jack Horner—sat in a corner—
            Up above the world so high—
            And all the king's horses—and all the king's men . . .

He nibbles his quill, is struck by an inspiration, and writes

            Kissed the girls and made them cry!

He stands in the middle of the stage, proudly surveying his work

Mrs Penguin (*moving to him*) Have you found that wand?

Minstrel Haven't been looking for it. Shall I read you my latest composition?

Mrs Penguin No. D'you know where the wand is, then?

Minstrel No. It's a very nice composition.

Mrs Penguin That's hardly likely. You'll be wanting an excuse, won't you—for not finding the wand? I've got some nice ones here. (*She indicates her tray*)

Minstrel (*haughtily*) I shall make up my own, thank you.

Mrs Penguin Oh—do-it-yourself, eh? Ah well—we know what will happen to you, don't we. You'll be walking on the black lines of the pavement.

Minstrel My superior intelligence, of course, will prevent me from suffering any such fate.

Mrs Penguin (*sniffing*) Well, I do hope so, I'm sure.

Minstrel (*turning, suddenly aware that he has seen, in the Reserve Cockatoo, something unusual*) Do you see what I see?

Mrs Penguin Depends on where I'm looking.

Minstrel The Cockatoo—he's actually *working*! Doing something useful—for a change!

Mrs Penguin Huh—about time, too. Can't stand them birds, myself. (*She starts to go*) Well, I must be off. I've got my excuses to sell, and if you don't want one . . .

   Mrs Penguin exits

The Reserve Cockatoo straightens to relieve his aching back, which he rubs with his downstage wing

Minstrel (*imperiously*) Carry on working, my good man. Carry on.

The Reserve Cockatoo resumes weeding, while the Minstrel proceeds to the centre of the raised bank

   Meanwhile, I shall divert you with one of my masterpieces. (*He strikes a pose on the bank, one foot higher than the other, unrolls his scroll, and announces*) A Love Story.

During the recitation the Reserve Cockatoo works slowly past the Minstrel

   The Lady Betsy Mary Jane
   Was very tall and somewhat plain.
   Sir Robin Richard Peter Prim

Was also tall—and rather slim.
(*To the Reserve Cockatoo*) That's quite good, don't you think?
They met each other, quite by chance,
While touring in the South of France.
She said she really wouldn't wed;
It drove the poor man off his head.
(*To the Reserve Cockatoo*) Getting exciting, isn't it?
They met again—'twas at a ball,
And so got married after all.
She turned out cross and rather snappy,
So even now they are not happy!
(*To the Reserve Cockatoo*) There! Isn't that lovely? Don't you think
I'm clever?

The Reserve Cockatoo pays not the slightest heed

Impertinent fellow! I'll wake you up, sir! (*He whistles like the Cockatoo*)

The Reserve Cockatoo turns. The Minstrel screeches, mock-Cockatoo, flaps his arms, and menaces the Reserve Cockatoo

The Reserve Cockatoo runs off

(*Preening himself*) W-e-ll, I've got that bird's measure at last, it seems. (*He gazes off*) Gone into the wood, has he? Good—I shall follow him. I've wanted to get even with him for years!

The Minstrel exits, as—

A drop-scene falls, representing the wood

SCENE 2

Down in the wood. Immediately following

The Lights change to a depth-of-the-forest effect. The Cockatoo, now costumed as the Gardener enters and perches on the log. He goes through the normal bird movements, beaking under his wing, etc. The Minstrel enters, searching for the Cockatoo

Minstrel Well, that's odd. I could have sworn he ran into this wood. (*He backs towards the Cockatoo, then turns*) Tell me, my good man, have you seen the Cockatoo around?

The Cockatoo eyes the Minstrel with his head on one side, then his head goes even further to the same side

Minstrel (*copying the head movement*) Well? Have you?

The Cockatoo suddenly bends his head to the other side

(*Following suit*) Oh, come on, man—say something!

The Cockatoo commences to sway from one foot to the other. The Minstrel is mesmerized into copying, then breaks off

Minstrel Oh, really—this is quite ridiculous! (*He sits on the end of the log*) This fellow is obviously of very low mentality.

The Cockatoo whistles

The Panjandrum enters, searching the ground for the wand

(*Turning to the Cockatoo*) At last! Well?

The Cockatoo screeches at the Minstrel and flaps his arms

The Minstrel, holding his hat on, flees off in panic, knocking the Panjandrum over

The Panjandrum immediately gets to his feet—only to be knocked over again by the Cockatoo who, with giant hops—both legs together—is trying to take off in flight after the Minstrel, using his arms as wings

The Cockatoo exits after the Minstrel

The Panjandrum is in an awful mess, his feet in the air, entangled in his robe, his crown off

Penny enters from the opposite side

Penny (*running to assist the Panjandrum*) Your Majesty! (*She helps him to his feet and dusts him down*) Whatever happened?

Panjandrum I'm not quite sure, your majesty—but I . . . (*He looks after the Cockatoo*) Oh dear, I hope no-one else saw me fall. I'm liable to be fined two-and-a-half pence if I'm seen being undignified in public. And now I've lost my crown! (*He searches in a panic*) I must find it! Everyone will be cross with me if I lose it. They'll make me pay for it out of my pocket-money.

Penny (*retrieving the crown*) Here it is, your Majesty.

Panjandrum Oh, thank you—thank you, miss—much obliged, I'm sure. (*He puts it on, it comes down over his eyes*)

Penny Oh, your Majesty—your crown is much too big.

Panjandrum (*with his head back, surveying Penny from below the crown*) Yes, it is a bit, isn't it, your Majesty. (*Pushing it back, he makes for the log, where he sits*) But I can't help it. You see, it's not really my crown.

Penny (*moving to the Panjandrum*) Not yours? You mean you're not really the king—er—Panjandrum—(*she makes a slight dip curtsy*)—your Majesty?

The Panjandrum rises, dips a curtsy in return, then sits again

Panjandrum Oh yes, your Majesty, I *am* the Panjandrum. But the crown originally belonged to my father. He was the last Panjandrum. And he was a big man—bigger than me—much.

Penny But surely you can afford a new crown—er—(*she curtsies*)—your Majesty?

D*

The Panjandrum rises, curtsies, sits

Panjandrum Alas, no, your majesty. I'm not allowed any money to buy one. I only get ten new pence a week pocket-money, and I really couldn't buy one out of that, could I, your majesty?

Penny Why do you keep calling me "your majesty"? You're "your Majesty"—er—(*she curtsies*)—your Majesty!

The Panjandrum is getting fed up with rising and curtsying, though he does it just the same

Panjandrum Oh, I wish you'd stop doing *this*! (*He times his curtsy with the word "this"*) It's so tiring—your majesty.

Penny But *you* are "your Majesty".

Panjandrum Am I?

Penny Yes.

Panjandrum Oh. No-one ever told me.

Penny That's what everyone should call *you*.

Panjandrum Ye-es—what a lovely idea! I never thought of that.

Penny It's time you put your foot down, your Majesty. You're a king.

Panjandrum Yes, I am, am't I? My foot down—with a firm hand!

Penny And just look at your clothes!

Panjandrum (*surveying himself*) Yes. I said my father was a big man, didn't I?

Penny No wonder you're in a mess, your Majesty.

Panjandrum In—(*waving an admonishing finger*)—a kerfuffle!

Penny Oh—yes—of course!

Panjandrum Tell me, your maj . . . —ahem—tell me, my child . . .

Penny That's better, your Majesty.

Panjandrum Have you found this wand we're all looking for?

Penny No, I'm afraid not. And I really must find it. How else can I get home?

Panjandrum Someone had better find it—otherwise we'll all be in trouble.

Mrs Penguin (*off, calling*) Excuses for sale!

Mrs Penguin enters

Excuses for sale! Elaborate excuses!

Panjandrum Ah, the very person we need!

Penny Mrs Penguin?

Panjandrum Mrs Penguin! She'll help us.

Mrs Penguin (*proffering a flag to Penny*) Buy an excuse, miss?

Penny I—I don't understand . . .

Panjandrum It's quite simple. We've all been told to find the wand. And if we don't, but can provide a satisfactory excuse for *not* finding it, then we won't have to walk on the black lines of the pavement.

Penny But that's silly!

Panjandrum Oh no, it's not. Mrs Penguin's family have been Excuse-Makers to the Panjandrum and the Royal Household for generations.

Mrs Penguin (*proudly*) Yes. By Appointment!

Panjandrum She can make up the most elaborate excuses at the shortest notice. (*To Mrs Penguin*) Can't you?

Mrs Penguin nods

Penny But I don't want an excuse. I want the wand!

Panjandrum Ah—but suppose you don't find the wand? An excuse from Mrs Penguin would save you from having to walk on the black lines of the pavement.

Mrs Penguin (*knowingly*) And we all know what that means, don't we? Do buy an excuse, miss—just a little one.

Penny An excuse won't get me home. And if I don't get home, I'll—I'll miss Christmas and—and everything!

Panjandrum How much are they?

Mrs Penguin Christmases?

Panjandrum No. Your excuses.

Mrs Penguin (*searching through her tray*) I have some very good ones at four-and-a-half pence.

The Panjandrum turns away to extract his handkerchief, wherein his money is tied. He counts it carefully and works out how much it will cost him on his fingers, during the following

Penny Whoever heard of excuses being kept in jars?

Mrs Penguin (*lifting and displaying a coloured jar*) Oh, these are not excuses, dear. These are promises. I always keep them in jars. Very brittle things, promises—so easily broken! (*She replaces the jar*) I get a great many broken promises as it is—you'd never believe! And then I have to sell them off cheap—like this. (*She holds up a small dish*) I sell them loose—Broken Promises, three a penny.

Penny D'you mean to say that you can actually sell broken promises?

Mrs Penguin Oh yes—there's sometimes quite a run on them—like washing behind one's ears, or going to bed before the telly closes down. But it's my excuses that sell best—especially with schoolchildren. (*Selecting individual flags*) Take this one, for instance—"Excuse for not doing homework". Or this—"Excuse for being late for school". Or this—"Excuse for not doing P.T."

Penny We-ell, these do sound useful!

Mrs Penguin Some of my customers buy dozens at a time—them as likes never to be without an excuse, that is. But my best-selling excuse at the moment is this one. (*She selects a flag*) "Excuse for not finding the wand." Would you like one?

Penny I'm afraid I haven't any money.

Panjandrum Allow me. (*To Mrs Penguin*) Have you any cheap ones?

Penguin I'm afraid my Flimsy Excuses are all gone. They were very cheap. Not worth much at all.

Panjandrum So what's your next price?

Mrs Penguin (*holding up a flag*) I have these—they're marked "Extra Good"—fourpence-ha'penny each. And I think I have some tuppenny ones—yes, here we are, but they're not nearly so good, although some people buy them.

Penny Who would want an excuse that wasn't any good?

Mrs Penguin Oh, you'd be surprised! Some people think any excuse is better than none—even if it's a bad one.

Panjandrum I'll have two at four-and-a-half pence, please. (*He drops the money in the tray*)

Mrs Penguin pins flags on both Penny and the Panjandrum

Mrs Penguin Thank you very much, sir. (*She goes off, calling*) Excuses for sale! Excuses for sale! Fine, fresh excuses!

Mrs Penguin exits. The Snowman enters from the opposite side

Snowman Ah, there you are! I've been looking for you.

Penny And I for you. And—oh, thank goodness—you've still got the wand!

Snowman Yes. (*He displays the wand*)

The Panjandrum looks at the wand most curiously

I've been having such fun with it. Watch this. (*He looks around, and sees the log*) I wish—I wish that log would disappear!

The log immediately whisks itself off

Panjandrum (*ruefully*) And I spent nearly all my pocket-money buying excuses!

Snowman Oh, that's not your biggest worry now—not by any means.

Panjandrum Why—what do you mean?

Snowman You should just see what's happening back at the Palace!

Panjandrum Why?

The drop-scene rises

SCENE 3

The Palace. The action is continuous

Apart from the Mandarin seated on the throne, and the Doctor-in-Law standing a step below, wringing his hands, the Palace is empty. All the other seats, and anything else that may have enhanced the scene previously, have gone

Panjandrum What's happened?

Doctor (*dropping on his knees*) Oh please, Great Panjandrum—forgive me!

The Gardener, still in the Cockatoo's costume, enters, menacing with a pitchfork

Gardener Where is he? Where is he?

Snowman (*hiding behind Penny*) Oh dear—I'm afraid it's me he's after!

The Cockatoo, still in the Gardener's costume, enters and perches on the front edge of the rostrum

Cockatoo (*with menacing bird motions at the Doctor-in-Law*) Down with him! Down with him!

Snowman (*retreating*) Oh very much dear! *He's* after me, too!

Panjandrum (*holding up his hand and snapping his fingers as if in a classroom*) Please! Please! Can I know what's happening, please?

Gardener I can tell ye what's happened . . .

Panjandrum (*moving between the Doctor-in-Law and the Gardener, and dipping a curtsy*) Yes—if you would be so good.

Cockatoo Down with doctors! Down with doctors!

Gardener I'll also tell ye what's *going* to happen! (*He jerks his pitchfork*) Git out o' me way!

Panjandrum (*stepping back quickly*) Oh—yes of course—certainly!

Penny Your Majesty! You're a king, remember. Be one!

Panjandrum Er—now?

Penny Yes. Now!

The Gardener is about to lunge at the Doctor-in-Law

Panjandrum (*holding up his hand, commandingly*) Stop!

The Gardener halts, amazed. There is a slight pause

Gardener Did you say that?

Panjandrum (*who has surprised himself*) Er—yes—I—er—(*he glances quickly behind himself both ways, to make sure*)—think so . . .

Cockatoo Down with everybody! Down with . . .

Panjandrum (*thundering*) *QUIET*, you—you silly little man, you!

The Cockatoo edges along the rostrum, opening and closing his mouth, bird-like, but saying nothing

(*To Penny, delighted*) It works! I can do it!

Penny Of course you can, your Majesty. (*She curtsies*)

The Panjandrum makes an imperial inclination of the head towards Penny, then turns to the Mandarin

Panjandrum And now, will you please tell me what you are doing on my throne?

Mandarin (*nodding*) Yes, please.

Panjandrum What's going on here?

Gardener I can tell ye.

Panjandrum (*dangerously*) I can tell ye—what?

Gardener I can tell ye—(*bowing*) your Majesty!

Panjandrum That's better. (*To—Penny, delighted*) It really does work, doesn't it? I like it, I like it.

Penny gives the Panjandrum a full curtsy

(*Royal again*) Well—go on, my man.

Gardener (*indicating the Doctor-in-Law*) It's him, your Majesty.

Snowman (*joining Penny*) Thank goodness for that—I thought it was me he was after!

Panjandrum What has he done?

Cockatoo Down with him! Down with . . . (*He stops, on a glare from the Panjandrum*) Er—sorry, your Majesty.

Panjandrum I should think so, too.

Gardener Taxing us out of house and home, he is.

Panjandrum Taxing you? But we don't pay taxes in Kerfuffle!

Cockatoo We do now—your Majesty.

Gardener Yes—while you were away looking for that there wand. Tuppence, he wants—tuppence—for every worm I dig up. Why, it would cost me a fortune!

Cockatoo And another penny on every ounce of millet seed—that's what it's costing me!

Panjandrum Dis-graceful!

Gardener But it's not only that. Twelve-and-a-half pence a day it costs—just to get up!

Cockatoo And another fourteen pence to go to bed.

Gardener Three-and-a-half pence for every time you change your mind—

Cockatoo —and a penny for every time you sit down.

Panjandrum (*to the Doctor-in-Law*) Is this true?

The Doctor-in-Law nods miserably

And if you're doing that to them, what are you doing to everyone else? Where is everyone, anyway? My citizens—the—er—Crocodile . . .?

Doctor He's—er—in prison.

Panjandrum In prison? What for?

Doctor Not paying his taxes.

Panjandrum And the Seals—what about them?

Doctor In prison.

Panjandrum What are they in for?

Doctor Not paying their taxes.

Panjandrum And the Minstrel?

The Doctor-in-Law nods sadly

Panjandrum In prison?

The Doctor-in-Law nods sadly

Panjandrum Taxes?

The Doctor-in-Law nods sadly

Panjandrum This will never do. Who's the Great Panjandrum here? (*He mounts the rostrum to beside the Mandarin, speaking to him*) You or me?

Mandarin (*nodding*) Yes, please.

Doctor It was his idea, your Majesty!

Panjandrum Was it, indeed?

Mandarin (*nodding, pleased*) Yes, please.
Panjandrum Well, you don't intend to stay there, on my throne, do you—now that I'm back?
Mandarin Yes, please.
Gardener You're not our king!
Mandarin Yes, please.
Panjandrum How can we get him down out of here?
Penny Please, your Majesty—he's a Nodding Mandarin.
Panjandrum I can see that. He'll be nodding his head right off in a minute. Fetch the policeman!
Doctor You can't.
Panjandrum Why not? Is he in prison, too?
Doctor Er—not quite.
Panjandrum Where is he, then?
Doctor In bed.
Panjandrum In bed? What's he doing there?
Doctor He—er—he can't afford to get up.
Panjandrum Taxes?

The Doctor-in-Law nods

Panjandrum Oh, this is terrible. (*To the Mandarin*) You can't run a country like this!
Mandarin Yes, please.
Penny Your Majesty—don't you see? He can only say "Yes".
Gardener I'll make him say something else—sharpish! Just one little jab, your Majesty—one little jab!
Cockatoo Hear, hear! Hear, hear!
Snowman I know how to get him out of there. Allow me. (*Waving the wand*) I wish for—Chop Suey—Chow Mein—Sweet-and-sour pork!

The Lights flicker as a tea-trolley with appropriate dishes comes rolling smoothly on

(*To the Mandarin, indicating the trolley, invitingly "headwaiterish"*) Chop Suey? Chow Mein? Sweet-and-sour pork?
Mandarin (*descending from the throne, hands in sleeves*) Yes, please. (*As he nears the trolley he withdraws chopsticks from his sleeves and proceeds to eat*)

The trolley moves slowly off; the Mandarin follows, still eating

The Panjandrum sits on the throne and beckons to the Snowman

Panjandrum Come here, my good man. What is your name?
Snowman Mr Fotheringay—your Majesty.
Panjandrum Kneel before us.

The Snowman kneels. The Panjandrum takes his sceptre from the rear of the throne seat and lightly touches each shoulder of the Snowman

Arise, Sir Mister Fotheringay!

All applaud. The Snowman rises. The Cockatoo, behind the Gardener, whistles

Gardener (*turning*) Er—yes?

The Cockatoo screeches and flaps his arms at the Gardener

The Gardener flees off, pursued by the Cockatoo

Snowman Oh dear—that's something I must put right. (*He waves the wand*) I wish—I wish them back as they were!

The Cockatoo runs across the stage, pursued by the Gardener.

The following two speeches are spoken simultaneously—thus keeping the voices right for the original characters, though in fact the Cockatoo—still dressed as the Gardener, crosses the stage first, pursued by the Gardener—dressed as the Cockatoo

Gardener Get that bird off me, somebody! Dang me if I don't get his tail-feathers, one o' these days! (*Speaking*

Cockatoo Down with gardeners! That's what I say—down *together*) with them all! Down with gardeners!

Snowman Situation normal! (*To Penny, taking her hand and leading her downstage*) Penny . . .

Penny Yes?

Snowman We still haven't found the Fairy!

During the above five speeches the Fish enters along the rostrum, dragging his shopping trolley, now full, behind him and reading his comic

He is wearing his top-hat, and very nearly bumps into the throne, which is in his line of travel. Realizing the Panjandrum is sitting there, he bows—out of his hat—and retreats backwards, still bowing

The Fish exits the way he came, pushing his trolley behind him. His hat, however, does not stop, but continues steadily on the Fish's original line of travel and, at the same even pace, exits the opposite side

The Panjandrum does a double-take on seeing the hat. As soon as the hat has gone, the inner tabs close, leaving Penny and the Snowman downstage

Scene 4

Another part of the wood. The action is continuous

Snowman (*continuing his previous speech. To the audience*) Had you forgotten? About the Fairy, I mean? I'll bet most of you had! But never mind. Maybe we can get her back again—if you believe, that is. (*To Penny*) Do you believe in fairies now, Penny?

Penny I—er—I don't know. I—I just—don't know.

Snowman You must believe in something.
Penny Must I?
Snowman Everyone should. In something good. I do.
Penny What do you believe in?
Snowman Well—there are lots of things. (*He sings*)

SONG—YOU'VE GOT TO BELIEVE

You've got to believe
In something.
You've got to have faith
In someone.
For the man without belief or faith
Is a man with sadness on his face,
So you've got to believe—
You've got to have faith!

You've got to believe
That sometime—
You've got to have faith
That somewhere—
That sometime, somewhere, someone will
Fulfil that wish you're wishing still,
So you've got to believe!
You've got to have faith!

You've got to believe
That some day—
You've got to have faith
In some way—
That all your dreams and wishes, too,
Will every single one come true—
But you've got to believe!
You've got to have faith!

Penny So what do we do about it?
Snowman About what?
Penny Well—the Fairy.

The Snowman moves away, thinking, then turns, inspired

Snowman Simple! (*He holds up the wand*) The answer's right here, in my hand. (*He holds the wand erect, both hands round it, almost praying again*) I wish—I wish—I wish the Fairy back again!

Nothing happens

Penny Nothing happened. Now what do we do?
Snowman Maybe she couldn't get here. Maybe she's so far away, she didn't get the message. I know what we'll do. (*To the audience*) If we all shout together, maybe she'll hear us. Are you willing to try? (*To Penny*) Penny—you take that side of the house and I'll take this.

They move to opposite sides of the stage

(*To the audience*) Now—I want everyone on this side of the house to shout out, with me, "Where's the Fairy gone?" And then you clap your hands twice, like this. (*He claps his hands loudly, twice*)

Penny And on this side of the house, we'll reply—(*loudly*)—"Far, far away!" (*She claps twice*)

Snowman And just to make sure, we'll do it twice. O.K.?

Penny O.K.

Snowman (*to his half of the audience*) Ready? With me. (*He calls*) Where's the Fairy gone? (*Clap, clap*) Where's the Fairy gone? (*Clap, clap*)

Penny (*conducting her half of the audience*) Far, far away! (*Clap, clap*) Far, far away. (*Clap, clap*)

They both glance round the stage

Snowman That's funny—there's no sign of her. Maybe she didn't hear us. (*To the audience*) Let's try again—but louder this time. Raise the roof! Ready? (*He conducts*) Where's the Fairy gone? (*Clap, clap*) Where's the Fairy gone? (*Clap, clap*)

Penny (*conducting*) Far, far away! (*Clap, clap*) Far, far away! (*Clap, clap*)

Snowman (*glancing round*) Oh dear—no Fairy yet. I can't understand it.

Penny I can—I think . . .

Snowman Well?

Penny We're making such a noise, perhaps we're frightening her.

Snowman Y-e-s—you could be right. In that case, let's try it in a whisper. And instead of clapping our hands this time, we'll snap our fingers— like this. (*He snaps his fingers twice. To his half of the audience*) Shall we try it? Come on. (*In a low voice*) Where's—the Fairy—gone? (*Snap, snap*) Where's—the Fairy—gone? (*Snap, snap*)

Penny (*conducting, in a low voice*) Far—far—away. (*Snap, snap*) Far—far —away. (*Snap, snap*)

Snowman (*glancing round again*) And still no Fairy! (*To the audience*) Let's try it just once more, and very, *very* quietly this time. I hardly want to hear you! (*He conducts, little more than mouthing the words*) Where's—the Fairy—gone? (*Snap, snap*) Where's—the Fairy—gone? (*Snap, snap*)

Penny (*conducting, breathing the words only*) Far—far—away. (*Snap, snap*) Far—far—away. (*Snap, snap. She looks around. To the Snowman*) I'm afraid it's no good, Mr Fotheringay. She's gone for good.

Snowman (*a light dawning*) Oh no, she's not! I'm a duffer. (*To Penny*) You're a duffer! (*To the audience*) You're all duffers!

Penny Why, what do you mean?

Snowman What was it I wished? What did I actually *say*?

Penny You said—(*remembering*)—"I wish—I wish the Fairy back again!"

Snowman That's right.

Penny So?

Snowman But I didn't say where, did I? And where *should* the Fairy be? A Christmas tree fairy? (*To the audience*) Do *you* know! That's right—

on the Christmas tree! (*Taking Penny's hand*) Shall we go home now, Penny, and find out?
Penny Oh yes, please!

Penny and the Snowman run off together

The Lights fade to a Black-out as the inner tabs open

SCENE 5

Penny's garden. Dawn

The Christmas tree fairy is pin-point spotted on the tree in the window, possibly revolving. As the dawn breaks, the fairy stops revolving. All is now as in the opening scene of the play, with two exceptions. There is no Snowman, but on a lower slope of the bank there is a single clump of snowdrops. Beside the snowdrops lie a battered top-hat and a carrot. The Christmas bells of a distant church can be heard—they gradually fade

Penny (*off, calling*) Mr Fotheringay! Mr Fotheringay! It's Christmas.

Penny enters carrying a kitten, on which all her attention is centred

Merry Christmas, Mr Fotheringay—and look what I've got. A kitten! My very own kitten. My wish come true! (*She looks up for the Snowman*) Oh—he's gone. (*She moves to pick up the hat and carrot*) Poor Mr Fotheringay! Why did you have to go? (*She looks up at the sky*) Though I suppose you had to—it's not nearly so cold today. But I wish you'd stayed—just to see you, Kitty. (*She is about to depart, when she notices the snowdrops. She gives a slight gasp and goes to them, crouching*) He *did* stay! Look, Kitty—a snowdrop. His wish came true, too! He wanted to be a flower—and he is! Oh, I'm so glad—so glad his wish came true. (*She turns to go*) And as for these—his hat and his nose—I shall keep them for ever and ever!

The unaccompanied voice of the Snowman is heard singing off, slowly, plaintively

THE SNOWMAN'S SONG (reprise)

Snowman   With my hat upon my head,
          And my carrot-nose so red,
          I have two glass eyes,
          And—surprise, surprise—
          For buttons, I have stones instead!

Penny (*to the audience*) I can't believe he's really gone, can you? Let's bring him back again! Help me. (*She chants*) We want the Snowman! (*She starts conducting the audience*) We want the Snowman! We want the Snowman! *ad lib.*

The Snowman enters, to music, with his little song and dance

Snowman So if you meet me in the snow
Don't forget to say "Hullo!"
Like a Christmas card,
It's not very hard
To spread a little, friendly glow!

As Penny and the Snowman wave—

the CURTAIN *falls*

FURNITURE AND PROPERTY LIST

ACT I

SCENE 1

On stage: Snowy bank. *On it:* snow-covered tree (see Production Notes)
House frame with window. *Inside:* decorated Christmas tree (see
    Production Notes)
On ground: "snow"

Off stage: Lantern **(Carol Singers)**
Dish of ice-cream and spoon **(Penny)**

Personal: **Snowman:** plastic foam for snow effect
Penny: coin, wristwatch
Fairy: wand

SCENE 2

On stage: Armchair
Settee
Chair. *On it:* wellington boot
Wardrobe
Bed
Electric fire
Fireplace. *On mantelpiece:* ornaments, including Nodding Mandarin,
    hanging stocking
Christmas tree (from Scene 1, without fairy). *On floor under it:* wand
All round the room: clothing, comics, hockey-stick, general jumble of
    Penny's possessions (see Production Notes)

ACT II

SCENE 1

On stage: Rostrum with steps, covered with grass matting
Hedge
Bush
Log. *Behind it:* slate, piece of chalk

Off stage: Fishing-rod **(Fish)**
Shopping basket **(Mrs Penguin)**
Garden shears **(Gardener)**
Bowler hat (hidden by bank, for **Fish** to "catch")

Personal: **Doctor:** very large watch, notebook, pencil stub
Penny: small piece of paper
Minstrel: long walking-stick, scroll
Crocodile: clown's "eye-fountains" (optional)

Scene 2

On stage: Nil
Personal: **First Seal:** letter in envelope

Scene 3

On stage: Throne
1 high seat or thronelet (see Production Notes)
9 stools or chairs
Optional pillars, carpet, step (see Production Notes)

Off stage: Gavel **(Doctor)**
Coloured ball, ball-and-cup toy or feather duster **(Panjandrum)**
Yo-yo **(Mandarin)**

Personal: **Minstrel:** scroll

ACT III

Scene 1

On stage: As Act II, Scene 1
Log set downstage (see Production Notes)
Weeds on ground

Off stage: Comic **(Fish)**
Empty shopping trolley **(Fish)**
Basket **(Gardener)**
Wand **(Snowman)**
Flag tray with flag-day-type flags, small coloured jars, "EXCUSES"
notice **(Mrs Penguin)**

Personal: **Minstrel:** open scroll, quill

Scene 2

On stage: Log (from Scene 1)

Personal: **Panjandrum:** money wrapped in handkerchief

SCENE 3

On stage: **Panjandrum's** throne. *Hidden in it:* sceptre

Off stage: Pitchfork **(Gardener)**
Tea-trolley with Chinese foods (see Production Notes)
Shopping trolley filled with goods **(Fish)**

Personal: **Mandarin:** chopsticks

SCENE 5

On stage: As Act I, Scene 1
On bank: clump of snowdrops, battered top-hat, carrot

Off stage: Kitten **(Penny)**

MUSIC PLOT

NOTE: if the players do not sing, all the lyrics in the play can be entirely spoken against the background of the appropriate music.

ACT I

The Snowman's Song	**Snowman**
The Hap-Hap-Happy Song	**Snowman**
If You Want To Find a Thing	**Snowman**

ACT II

The Seals' Song (and reprises)	**Seals**

ACT III

The Snowman's Song (reprise)	**Snowman**
You've Got To Believe	**Snowman**
The Snowman's Song (reprise)	**Snowman**

The music for this play can be obtained from Samuel French Ltd

LIGHTING PLOT

NOTE: This may be elaborated as facilities permit
Property fittings required: Christmas tree lights (optional), electric fire

ACT I, SCENE 1

To open: General effect of winter moonlight. Light shining from house window.
Tree lights on in house

Cue 1	**Penny** closes window	(Page 4)
	Snap off house light, gradually darken overall lighting	
Cue 2	**Snowman:** "Wish me the fairy!"	(Page 6)
	Torch or pin-point spot on house tree fairy	
Cue 3	**Snowman:** "Wish hard—hard!"	(Page 6)
	Momentary Black-out. Take out house tree lights, snap	
	on garden tree lights	
Cue 4	**Snowman:** "I believe in fairies"	(Page 6)
	Pin-point spot on garden tree fairy	
Cue 5	**Snowman:** "Yes, please, come down."	(Page 6)
	Momentary Black-out. Pin spot flies around, to window	
	*ledge and back, then to **Fairy's** entrance and enlarges.*	
	Bring up overall lighting to opening	
Cue 6	**Fairy:** "Did you expect it to?"	(Page 9)
	Gradually darken overall lighting	
Cue 7	**Fairy** waves wand and disappears	(Page 9)
	Momentary Black-out. Reverse tree lights	

ACT I, SCENE 2

To open: General warm interior lighting. Electric fire lit

Cue 8	**Penny** switches off fire	(Page 10)
	Snap off electric fire	
Cue 9	**Snowman:** "... IN AN AWFUL KERFUFFLE!"	(Page 14)
	Flashing lights, rapid changes of colour, tree lights on and off	
	—continue until CURTAIN *falls*	

ACT II, SCENE 1

To open: Flashes, colour changes, etc., as close of Act I

Cue 10	As opening effects quieten down	(Page 16)
	Resolve into overall exterior daylight	

ACT II, SCENE 2

To open: Lighting concentrated downstage

No cues

ACT II, SCENE 3

To open: Overall daylight effect

Cue 11   **Fish** exits   (Page 39)
             Fade to spot on **Penny**

ACT III, SCENE 1

To open: Overall daylight effect

Cue 12   **Snowman:** ". . . know what I'm wishing for!"   (Page 41)
             *All lights dip. Dips increase in length, culminating in
                temporary Black-out—then return to former lighting*

ACT III, Scene 2

To open: Effect of dim forest depths
No cues

ACT III, SCENE 3

To open: Overall lighting up to cover Palace

Cue 13   **Snowman:** ". . . sweet-and-sour pork!"   (Page 51)
             Lighting flickers

ACT III, SCENE 4

To open: Lighting concentrated downstage

Cue 14   **Penny** and **Snowman** exit   (Page 55)
             Quick fade to Black-out

ACT III, SCENE 5

To open: Effect of dawn—gradually brightening. Pin-point spot on
                house tree fairy

No cues

EFFECTS PLOT

ACT I

SCENE 1

Cue 1   **Snowman:** "Wish hard—hard!"   (Page 6)
Reverse trees in Black-out

Cue 2   **Fairy** exits   (Page 9)
Reverse trees in Black-out

SCENE 2

Cue 3   **Penny** points wand   (Page 11)
Start "magical" props movements

Cue 4   **Snowman:** "I WISH TO BE IN AN AWFUL   (Page 14)
       KERFUFFLE!"
Deep gong note, whistles, weird sounds, swishes, exciting
music—continue until CURTAIN *falls*

ACT II

SCENE 1

Cue 5   **Penny:** "Where are we?"   (Page 16)
Hint of Eastern music

SCENE 2

Cue 6   **Second Seal:** "No thank you!"   (Page 28)
Deep gong sounds 3 times

SCENE 3

Cue 7   **Seals** and **Cockatoo** sway   (Page 30)
Fanfare, followed by processional music

Cue 8   **Mandarin** rises   (Page 35)
Snatch of Eastern music

ACT III

SCENE 1

Cue 9   **Snowman:** ". . . what I'm wishing for!"   (Page 41)
Deep gong notes, whistles, weird sounds, swishes, exciting
music—continue through Black-out

SCENE 2

Cue 10   **Snowman: ". . . log would disappear!"**   (Page 48)
           Log is whisked off

SCENE 3

Cue 11   **Snowman: ". . . sweet-and-sour pork!"**   (Page 51)
.   *Tea-trolley glides on stage: and off as* **Mandarin** *eats from it*

SCENE 4

No cues

SCENE 5

Cue 12   As Scene opens   (Page 55)
           Christmas church bells—slowly fading

MADE AND PRINTED IN GREAT BRITAIN BY
LATIMER TREND & COMPANY LTD PLYMOUTH

MADE IN ENGLAND